GROWING YOUR OWN BUSINESS: A WORKBOOK

RON IMMINK & BRIAN O'KANE

LINKED TO

WWW.GROWINGABUSINESSINIRELAND.COM

WWW.SPOTCHECKONLINE.COM

www.oaktreepress.com

YOUR SPOTCHECK® VOUCHER ID IS: 0E45-465A-8E86-691F

INTERTRADEIRELAND
THE TRADE AND BUSINESS DEVELOPMENT BODY

InterTradeIreland's mission, as set out in its Corporate Plan 2002-2004 and based on its legislative remit, is "to lead the development of the island economy through distinctive knowledge-based interventions which will produce significant returns in the areas of cross-border trade and business development".

InterTradeIreland's strategic framework is built on the use of knowledge to accelerate trade and business development across the island economy.

Priority Programme Areas

InterTradeIreland has identified eight priority programmes through which it will deliver a number of initiatives to benefit North/South trade and business development. Our priority programmes include the following key projects:

- Trade Development
  - > *Acumen* - an all-island trade programme designed to increase the level of cross-border trade by participating companies.
  - > *Focus* - an all-island sales and marketing initiative using graduates to identify new markets and deliver increased sales for their host companies.
  - > *Public Procurement* - a series of actions to help indigenous businesses to exploit the island-wide €11.5Bn Public Procurement market opportunities.
- Trade Awareness
  - > *Awards Events* - continue to support high-profile Awards Events to promote best practice and the development of networks across the island.
  - > *Business Forums* - a series of forums run across the island on cross-jurisdiction business matters, in areas such as legal and financial matters.
- Micro-Enterprise Support
- Business and Economic Research
- EquityNetwork - promoting awareness and exploitation of private equity to drive business growth
- Science and Technology
  - > *Expertise Ireland* - the introduction of an all-island research portal, facilitating the sharing of knowledge on research.
  - > *Fusion* - a three-way technology-transfer project involving science graduates, businesses and research institutes with a cross-border focus.
  - > *The Digital Island* - a project designed to drive the fullest exploitation of digital technologies in E-Commerce, ICT Infrastructure & Services and Government Support to Business.
- All-Island Benchmarking
- Supply Chain and Cluster Development.

CONTACT DETAILS

InterTradeIreland
The Old Gasworks Business Park, Kilmorey Street, Newry, Co. Down BT34 2DE
Northern Ireland
Email: info@intertradeireland.com **Web:** www.intertradeireland.com
Tel: + 44 28 3083 4100 (From Rep. of Ireland: 048 3083 4100)
Fax: + 44 28 3083 4155 (From Rep. of Ireland: 048 3083 4155)

*Inter*Trade*Ireland*
TRADE & BUSINESS DEVELOPMENT BODY

EQUITYNETWORK

EquityNetwork is the outcome of comprehensive research undertaken in 1999 by InterTradeIreland into private equity provision on this island. The findings revealed a dramatic increase in the amounts of private equity raised and invested in the past decade. However, regions outside of Dublin showed slower signs of growth and a low level of uptake. This disparity is due primarily, not to short supply of funds, but to a shortage of quality deals, despite a strong demand. The research also highlighted a gap in the supply of equity finance to early stage start-up projects. This is not peculiar to the local market but reflects the high level of risk of funding such projects and the acost of managing the investment, relative to the actual funds invested.

To address this shortfall, InterTradeIreland developed EquityNetwork - a detailed education and awareness programme on the benefits and availability of private equity.

More Resources for Business

Promoting private equity is the key to accelerating business growth among new ventures, small and expanding businesses and inward investors. Based at InterTradeIreland's offices, EquityNetwork provides the following services to the business community:

* An island-wide education programme to raise the awareness and use of private equity for accelerating business growth.
* Free, value-added advisory services to businesses to assist in making them 'investor-ready'.
* Signposting and advice for businesses seeking equity finance.
* The promotion and development of a comprehensive island-wide non-executive director network available to businesses.
* An island-wide Centre-of-Excellence on private equity and related matters.

CONTACT DETAILS

EquityNetwork
InterTradeIreland, The Old Gasworks Business Park, Kilmorey Street, Newry, Co. Down BT34 2DE, Northern Ireland
Email: equity@intertradeireland.com **Web:** www.intertradeireland.com
Tel: + 44 28 3083 4151 (From Rep. of Ireland: 048 3083 4151)
Fax: + 44 28 3083 4155 (From Rep. of Ireland: 048 3083 4155)

Promoting Private Equity to Accelerate Business Growth

PREFACE

Welcome to **Growing Your Own Business: A Workbook**.

Who is this Workbook for?

Growing Your Own Business: A Workbook aims to help you to develop your business. It is intended to be read and used by owner/managers and management teams of small businesses, who are keen to grow those businesses. By small businesses, we mean businesses with probably fewer than 30 employees – certainly fewer than 100 employees – but, more importantly, businesses that lack the range of functional specialists and specialisms – marketing, sales, production, finance, administration, etc – that are commonplace in larger businesses. The total day-to-day involvement of the owner/manager, more than the number of employees, is the defining characteristic of Irish businesses that are most ready, most welcoming and most needy of growth.

Structure & Content

There are four sections in this workbook:

- **Section 1: Where Do You Want To Be?** looks to the future of your business. It's part dream, part vision, part decision – the equivalent of deciding to sail around the world. It's a "first cut", a draft of your eventual strategy, since any strategy must take into account the real world in which it is to be implemented. Therefore, your initial thoughts on strategy may be amended several times as you work through this workbook. Nonetheless, it is important that you stake an early direction for your business. After all, if you don't know where you want to go, how will you work out how to get there – let alone know when you have arrived?

- **Section 2: Where Are You Now?** involves a review of your business as it is today. It's not intended to be an exhaustive analysis, merely a starting point. This is important to identify the strengths and weaknesses of your business now, where it is likely to face challenges – either opportunities or threats – in the future, and the resources that it has available to meet these challenges.

- **Section 3: How Do You Get to Where You Want To Be?** uses Oak Tree Press' **SPOTcheck®** online assessment tool to identify the growth potential of your business, as well as the interventions that may be appropriate to eliminate weaknesses, build on strengths, maximise opportunities and avoid threats. In this section, you build the strategy that will direct the growth of your business through information and exercises, which guide you and your management team to think through all the issues involved in growth. Each chapter in this section ends with an exercise on the resource implications of your ideas and plans for growth – this provides you with inputs into your business plan.

- **Section 4: Business Planning** deals with the development of a business plan for your business. It is based on your decisions made in **Sections 1 (Where Do You Want To Be?)** and **3 (How Do You Get to Where You Want To Be?)** of the workbook. This section starts by distinguishing between the process of business planning and the output from the process – the business plan document. Individual chapters deal with the preparation of financial projections, the writing of text for a business plan document, and the accumulation of evidence to support assumptions, assertions and figures in a business plan. Break-even, ratio, sensitivity and "what if?" analysis are used to refine financial projections and to identify the business' true funding gap and how it can be filled. The final chapter shows how to tailor the contents of a business plan to different audiences.

Finally, at the back of the workbook, you will find Appendices that provide useful information and links to resources, as well as an access code for the **SPOTcheck®** online assessment tool.

How to Use this Workbook

"Growth", like "success", requires definition, if it is to act as a target. This issue is considered in **Section 1: Where Do You Want To Be?.**

Growth requires commitment. Unless a business is very lucky, growth does not happen of its own accord. It happens as a result of a decision or decisions, based ideally on a process of thinking and planning. It requires vision, desire, skills and resources – and above all, commitment.

Commitment means that this workbook is not an easy read – in fact, it's not for reading, it's for doing. It's a workbook. To maximize the value you gain from it, you must be prepared to work at thinking and planning how to grow your business. If you do, you will find that this workbook directs your thinking and offers you a straightforward and robust process for business planning that will contribute to the growth of your business.

Who Should Use this Workbook?

Throughout the workbook, we refer to the "promoters", the "management team", the "promoters/management team". In every case, we mean the owner/manager, any equity shareholder(s) actively involved in the business (spouses with nominal shareholdings for purely legal reasons are "family" not "management team") and key senior staff, whether or not they have an equity interest, whose continued involvement is critical to the business.

This means that the workbook needs to be read – and the exercises worked through – by at least two people and probably more. We suggest that you (the management team, however many you number) read and work through the exercises individually first and then come together as a team to discuss the results. You will be surprised both at the range of your insights and at the depth of some of them – probably from unexpected quarters. But all action towards the future development of the business must be decided as a team, with a complete buy-in from everyone. Rushing forward without total commitment may create the illusion of progress – but it will be very short-lived.

And, last, we have used "you" in the titles of the sections and throughout this workbook in order to place the responsibility for the growth of the business firmly where it belongs – on the shoulders of the owner/manager and their management team.

Acknowledgements
We have long had an ambition to write a book like **Growing Your Own Business: A Workbook**. We see it as a natural response to the reaction we have received over the past five years to our **Starting Your Own Business: A Workbook**, now effectively the standard for business planning for start-ups across Ireland. We are grateful to everyone who has used **Starting Your Own Business: A Workbook** and taken

the trouble to contact us with their feedback – for the many of you who have asked for a follow-up book, here it is now. We are also grateful to the enterprise support agencies, of which there are many, which have been universally supportive and encouraging of our efforts to provide Irish entrepreneurs North and South with the information, advice and resources that they need to succeed.

In planning to write **Growing Your Own Business: A Workbook**, we approached InterTradeIreland, the North/South body with responsibility for cross-border business development, and EquityNetwork. From the beginning, both organisations were enthusiastic and supportive. It is largely through their funding that we were able to devote the time to writing this workbook and developing the website, **www.growingabusinessinireland.com**. We are grateful to all at InterTradeIreland and EquityNetwork for their encouragement.

We are also grateful to the CEOs of the County Enterprise Boards, Enterprise NI and InvestNI and the many other people in enterprise support organisations, North and South, who took the time and trouble to comment on drafts of this workbook. Thank you for your insights.

And, last, **SPOTcheck®**. We developed this assessment tool for the South Dublin County nterprise Board, to help its Evaluation Committee to decide on the assistance appropriate to each applicant business and to benchmark the business so that the value of the assistance provided could be assessed subsequently. After successful pilot implementations, SDCEB's chief executive, Loman O'Byrne, encouraged us to make **SPOTcheck®** available to a wider audience through the Internet. And so, **www.spotcheckonline.com** was born. As you will read later in the workbook, **SPOTcheck®** is designed to assess the growth potential of a business and, from that, to identify interventions that will help to eliminate weaknesses, build on strengths, maximise opportunities and avoid threats. It fits perfectly with the thrust of **Growing Your Own Business: A Workbook** and forms a key element in **Section 3: How Do You Get to Where You Want To Be?**. A free **SPOTcheck®** assessment is available with every copy of this workbook to encourage you to use it.

We have enjoyed writing **Growing Your Own Business: A Workbook** – for what we have learnt and for the people we have met in doing so. We hope you find it useful and rewarding. We wish you every success in developing your business.

Ron Immink
Brian O'Kane
November 2002

Section 1:
Where Do You Want To Be?

Answering the question "Where do you want to be?" is often the first stumbling block in growing a business. So the first problem is: In which direction is this future business? The second problem is: If you don't know what direction you should be going in (in other words, if you can't answer the previous question), how can you know that you are going in the *right* direction?

This section of the workbook is where you begin to define the parameters that shape your strategy. As you work through the later sections of this workbook – as you work through the process of business planning – these parameters will become more precise.

All the promoters and the full management team should complete the exercises in this part individually. Later, perhaps in a facilitated session, the results should be shared. Decisions should then be taken as a team.

KEY ISSUES

The key issues for attention are:

- Fit with life plan
- Values
- Passion
- Education, experience and skills
- Network
- Financial capacity.

All these contribute – in a unique mix for each business – to a sustainable competitive advantage.

The final issue has to do with time. Without a deadline, little happens. If you plan to grow your business, you must set a timescale—and manage it through an action plan.

GROWTH AS A JOURNEY

Growing a business is like setting sail on a round-the-world sea voyage. Even for a seasoned sailor, circumnavigating the globe adds new dimension. Weather, re-supply of food and water, re-fuelling, navigation, the length of time spent at sea, the need for the crew to work together well – all must be considered.

And then there's the type of boat – and the equipment it will need – to be taken into account. The risks are enormous and the whole exercise needs careful planning, if it is not to end in disaster.

Your starting point might be to pull out an atlas at home and to begin to outline a route. Next, you might consult various authorities on whether this route was feasible, whether it was the best/fastest/shortest/most interesting, and what resources you might need. More detailed planning will require better maps. And list-making will begin, to control the thousand and one details that must be thought of.

There's several months work in all this – and significant cost. Your next thoughts would be how to pay for everything – from your own resources initially, from sponsorship, etc.

And the end result would be a detailed plan, setting exactly how you would get from your home in Ireland around the world and back again safely, acquiring all the equipment and information that you need to do so. That plan would be pored over, revised and amended many times before you set off.

But the real world has a nasty habit of interfering with plans. So you need to build flexibility into your planning. This involves thinking ahead and working out what might go wrong – and then planning to prevent it or to mitigate its consequences. You draw on your own experience, if it is relevant, and that of others who have "been there, done that". And, thus, you develop a plan that is robust enough to survive the real world.

No-one finds it surprising that a round-the-world sea voyage requires such detailed planning. It's a once in a life-time exercise, something that few people have experience of, and the risks and potential for disaster are very clear. So there's little need to convince anyone of the need to plan. But growing a business needs the same kind of careful, thoughtful preparation. This section of the workbook starts the thinking process.

OBJECTIVE

- To identify the issues involved in growth
- To understand the need for planning

OBJECTIVE

- To understand your personal parameters/ context
- To define your values
- To define your passions
- To understand your skill levels
- To map your personal network
- To define your personal financial parameters

The first stage in developing growth plans for your business is to determine where you want to go in a personal context – in other words, why you want to grow your business. You need to decide this in a personal context, before you can approach the business context – otherwise, the two may be out of sync, and lead to disaster.

FIT WITH LIFE PLAN

Given that you are about to embark on a lengthy period requiring significant commitment and sacrifice, it is important to establish (re-establish?) why you are involved in your business. The answers to "why?" must link to your life plan, to the things and people that are important to you and to your view of where you want to be personally in five years' or 10 years' time. The questions in the exercise below appear simple but the answers are critical to the future of your company. For example, if you have a young family and would like to spend more time with them, seeing them grow up, how will you cope with the tensions caused by working the many 14- or 16-hour days that may be necessary as you grow the business? Will you resent the lost time? Will your family resent it – and you?

If your aim is to retire in five years' time, with sufficient wealth not to need to work any more, can you achieve this by growing your business? Could you retire now and not need to work? Could you retire now – and manage with less income, or make up the shortfall by working part-time?

It is unlikely that you will be able to answer these questions on the spot. It may take you an hour or two — even a day or two — to think through your answers properly. Take plenty of time to think them through – take as long as you need. Ultimately, this is where you decide your future and that of your business. And make sure that you involve your spouse/partner and your family in your thinking.

YOUR OWN VALUES

Why are values important? Remember that you, the other promoters and the management team are key to the business. It follows then that the business must reflect your way of thinking, your way of life and your values. If you are uncomfortable with the way in which you must do business, or with the people or circumstances with which you have to deal, you will not be successful at your business. Therefore, you must make sure that the business is true to yourself, your beliefs, your ethics and your principles. Your own value

---

EXERCISE
FIT WITH LIFE PLAN

- What do you want out of life?
- Where do you want to be in five years' time?
- Where do you want to be in 10 years' time?
- Does all this fit with growing the business?
- Why do you want to stay involved in the company?

EXERCISE
YOUR VALUES

Identify your personal values by answering these questions:

- What is important to you?
- What do you believe in?
- What do you stand for?
- What aims in life do you have?
- How do you treat other people — especially in circumstances where you do not need to care about their reactions?
- What do ethics mean to you in your daily life?
- What do ethics mean to you in your business life?
- If you didn't have to earn a living, what would you do with your life?
- How do you define success?
- What do you think of people who have not achieved success:
  - > By your definition of success?
  - > By the marketplace/society's definition of success?
- How would you like to be remembered?

system is an important element in achieving growth within your business, since it is a key determinant of the future shape and future direction of your business. Identifying your value system and documenting it is a useful task at this stage in preparing to grow your own business. Try the exercise on the previous page.

YOUR OWN PASSION

Unless you are passionate about what you do in life — or in business — you will neither succeed at it nor enjoy it. There is a clear link between passion, drive and success: The more passion, the more drive, the more success.

EXERCISE
PASSION

- What are you passionate about in life? Why?
- What are you passionate about in your business? Why?
- Do growing your business and your passion(s) fit together? How? Why?

What are you passionate about in your business?

YOUR OWN EDUCATION, EXPERIENCE AND SKILLS

As your company develops, you will need different sets of skills. The skills you used several years ago to propel your company through the start-up and early growth phases are not the same as the skills you now need for growth and maturity. Growth requires not only a broader range of skills but also deeper understanding and ability in each.

You need to decide which areas of your business are most critical for its growth and analyse your own education, experience and skills (and that of your other promoters and management team) in each of these. Later, the SPOTcheck® assessment model will help you identify areas critical to business growth — so you may want to return to this exercise after completing the assessment.

I've worked with hundreds of entrepreneurs, and I've never met one who said, "I want to get rich" who did. The successful ones say, "I want to find a way to do animation faster" or "I'm really interested in adhesion".

PROF JON GOODMAN, University of Southern California

EXERCISE
EDUCATION, EXPERIENCE AND SKILLS — GAPS AND FILLING THEM

First summarise your education, experience and skills:

EDUCATION

Period	Institution	Course	Applicability to your business during growth stage

EXPERIENCE

Period	Organisation	Position/Responsibility	Applicability to your business during growth stage

SKILLS

Period	Source	Nature of skill	Applicability to your business during growth stage

Next, identify the areas critical for growth in your business – and how your education, experience and skills match and where gaps remain:

Area	Match of:			Gap	How to Fill the Gap
	Education	Experience	Skills		

YOUR OWN NETWORK

"It is not what you know, it is who you know", says the proverb. Like all proverbs, it contains a lot of truth in very few words.

A network of connections is an especially powerful tool in growing a business. Research among high achievers shows that one of the reasons for their success is the fact that they cultivate (that is, develop and use) a strong network of personal contacts. You already know how useful it is to have a personal introduction to someone you have not met before, or to have a contact or interest in common with someone you are meeting for the first time. Both these help to build trust – the core of every business and personal relationship. By being very deliberate in the way that you use your network of personal contacts, you can develop your business at a much quicker pace. You know people, who know other people, who know other people … and before you know it, you have personal introductions to new clients, investors, and suppliers. Your network is a unique strategic resource. Complete the exercise below to record your network and to identify how valuable it might be to you.

YOUR OWN FINANCIAL CAPACITY

How deeply the promoters and management team are willing/able to commit is often measured by their personal financial commitment to achieve growth within the business. Reduced salaries, perks foregone and especially capital injections are the order of the day.

But financial commitment is sometimes constrained by financial capacity. If an executive's home is already heavily-mortgaged, there is no spare borrowing capacity — whether the borrowing is needed to invest in growth within the business or to replace income from the business becomes immaterial. Equally, an executive whose income is fully required to service borrowings and/or a lifestyle that cannot be reduced will be unable to provide the business with the financial flexibility it may require.

And, in terms of capital, an executive lacking in free personal capital may be at a disadvantage as regards other members of the promoters and management team when it comes to investing the business' future. All these things can give rise to tensions and so are best laid out in the open early on. Record your financial commitments and available personal capital in the exercises.

EXERCISE
NETWORKING — WHO DO I KNOW AND HOW CAN THEY HELP TO BUILD MY BUSINESS?

Develop a profile of your own current network along the following lines.

Contact organisation	Contact individual	Nature of contact	Quality of contact	Value of this contact to your business during growth stage

---

NOTE: All exercises and forms are available for download and completion at **www.growingabusinessinireland.com**.

FROM PERSONAL TO BUSINESS

Now that you have considered these issues from a personal perspective – ideally, at first individually and later in a shared session as a management team – it's now time to move to the business level.

It's not possible to emphasise too strongly the need for a fit between your personal needs and ambitions and your business needs and ambitions. If they are out of sync, one or both will suffer. So this is the time to align them – or to decide that they cannot be aligned without compromise and that you are better to forego growth, at least for the present. This may mean leaving the management team, selling the business or your stake in it, or simply postponing thoughts of dramatic growth for another, more suitable occasion or for slower, less dramatic growth that is possible today. Whatever the options, if it needs to be done, do it now!

EXERCISE
WHAT FINANCIAL COMMITMENTS DO YOU HAVE?

- Household expenses   _____ per week/month
- Loan repayments   _____ per week/month
- Savings/pension   _____ per week/month
- Hobbies/holidays   _____ per week/month
- Other (list)   _____ per week/month
                      _____ per week/month
                      _____ per week/month
                      _____ per week/month
- Total financial commitments   _____ per week/month

How much could you reduce these to provide cash to develop the business? _____ per week/month

---

EXERCISE
PERSONAL CAPITAL

- How much money do you have saved?   _____
- What other valuable assets do you have?

- Could these be sold to help finance the growth of the company? ☐ Yes ☐ No
- If not, why not?

- If yes, how much would they realise?   _____
- Therefore, how much free capital do you have available for investment in the business?   _____

OBJECTIVE

- To understand the business parameters/context
- To define values, passion, mission, vision for the business
- To set targets for the business

These days growing my company feels like what happens when you play one of my kid's video games. You work like crazy to get to the next level, only to have the game become infinitely more complicated as a result.

JIM ANSARA, founder and CEO of Shawmut Design and Construction

A key decision that you and the management team must make at this stage is what you mean by "growth".

If asked "What is growth?", most people will reply along the lines of "Bigger, better, more profitable".

But "bigger" does not necessarily mean "more profitable" – in fact, many businesses sacrifice profitability in the short-term (and, sometimes, forever) in the rush to grow bigger and gain more market-share.

"Better" begs the question "In what way?". More responsive customer service, products with more features, services more suited to individual customers' needs, a nicer place to work – or any of these?

"More profitable" could mean "smaller" – fewer products/services, fewer markets, fewer customers, fewer locations, fewer staff, even a smaller management team – as you shed unprofitable parts of your existing business. Your personal values from the last chapter will help you to decide.

The first step is to imagine what your business could be – dream, have fun. Complete the exercise below, describing your future business.

Once you have a clear picture of the possible future of your business and what "growth" means in that context, the next question is how to get to that distant place. Not in terms of detailed implementation (yet – that comes later), but in outline.

Because there is so much uncertainty at this stage, you should define four statements for the business that will help clarify your thinking on its future shape and direction.

The statements are:

- The values statement
- The passion statement
- The vision statement
- The mission statement

Let's look at each in turn.

A VALUES STATEMENT FOR YOUR BUSINESS

To find out what is important to your company — what its "values" are, start by making an inventory of your company's "soul", as shown in the stories, symbols and trophies that matter to the people within it. Complete the exercise below.

EXERCISE
STORIES, SYMBOLS, AND TROPHIES

- What are the famous stories in your company?
- What are the symbols in your company?
- What trophies do you keep?
- What are the highlights of the company's history?
- What is your company proud of?
- What language is used in your company? (For example, how do you talk about customers and competitors?)

EXERCISE
YOUR FUTURE BUSINESS

- Where do you see your company in 10 years' time?
  (Be as visual as possible. Complete the exercise as if describing a photograph or a painting or a movie of yourself and your company.)

- What does "growth" mean to you in the context of your business' future?

- How will you know whether you have been successful in achieving growth?

Your business' values statement expresses its values and guiding principles. These are not abstract concepts, but practical realities, rooted in your own personal values, which determine the way your business is managed and operated.

For example, if your business develops computer games software, its values statement determines its position on issues such as:

- Extreme violence in the games it develops: Is violence acceptable at all? And, if so, what level of violence?

- Determining suitability of its games for young children: Will you adopt industry standards for suitability of content? Or work to higher standards?

- Epilepsy as result of playing computer games: Will you avoid features that may cause epilepsy — even in a tiny percentage of users? Or will you ignore the research?

Use the following exercises to consider your business' values.

What do your answers tell you about your business values?

As an example, a business might have this as its values statement:

"To be ethical, honest and fair in all our dealings with customers, staff and suppliers; to share the benefits of our success with the community within which we operate; and to provide a fair return to our shareholders."

Now write a values statement for your business.

EXERCISE
IDENTIFYING BUSINESS VALUES

Rank the following in their order of importance to you in a business context:
(1= not important, 10 = very important):
- Personal development
- Maximum profit
- Creating employment
- Sustainable development
- Satisfying customers
- Beating the competition
- Raising your children
- The environment
- Developing good relationships
- Developing new products.

Based on your answers above, how would you deal with the following scenarios:
- You discover that a supplier has been under-billing you for the last 8 months. Will you inform them, knowing that as a result you will have to pay the difference? ☐ Yes ☐ No
- Your company has an important deadline to meet. One of the key people on the project must work overtime, but will miss a child's birthday as a result. Who would you regard as the "better" employee:
  > The employee who declines to work overtime and instead attends the birthday party ☐
  > The employee who willingly agrees to work overtime. ☐
- You find that your packaging might cause an allergic reaction to a very small group of users. Redesign of the packaging will put a strain on your profit margins. Will you redesign the packaging? ☐ Yes ☐ No

---

EXERCISE
A VALUES STATEMENT FOR YOUR BUSINESS

Write a values statement for your business that explains the values that you will aspire to in your dealings with:
- Customers
- Staff
- Suppliers
- Public/Community in general
- Shareholders.

Values are where the hard stuff and the soft stuff come together.

ROBERT HAAS, CEO, Levi Strauss

A PASSION STATEMENT FOR YOUR BUSINESS

The notion of a passion statement is drawn from Charles Handy's recent book, *The Elephant and the Flea*, in which he recognises the importance of passion as a contributory factor to successful growth. We have seen its importance from a personal perspective in earlier exercises.

What is your company passionate about?

- Quality?
- Customer service?
- Having the latest piece of equipment?

For example, a hotel might have a passion statement like this:

> "Our passion is customer service: To meet and exceed our guests' expectations in every contact."

A management consultancy might have the following passion statement:

> "Our passion is problem-solving: Solving our clients' problems quickly, efficiently, effectively, innovatively – and in a way that our client can take immediate ownership of the solution."

Use the following exercise to help you to draft your company's passion statement.

Our [original] vision: Meet payroll next week.
Charles Wang, CEO, Computer Associates

A VISION STATEMENT FOR YOUR BUSINESS

The vision statement explains your business as you expect it to be in 10 or 15 years' time. This is how you communicate your targets.

Your targets may be ambitious, but all good targets are. They must be achievable, but not too easily. They must set a broad description that challenges everyone working within the business. And, finally, targets must be measurable.

It is your vision statement that makes your targets clear.

For example, your vision statement might be:

> "To be one of the 10 largest accountancy practices in the country by the year 2015."

> "To own and operate a chain of 20 profitable computer re-selling stores in more than 10 key cities by 2015."

Before developing a vision statement for your business, you should look back at the exercise **Your Future Business** (page 8).

You should also consider future trends in your industry. These will help you to determine your ambition for your business in 10 or 15 year's time?

Now write a vision statement for your business.

EXERCISE
A PASSION STATEMENT FOR YOUR BUSINESS

Write a passion statement for your business, setting out what it is that your business is passionate about.

EXERCISE
A VISION STATEMENT FOR YOUR BUSINESS

Write a vision statement for your business, which sets out what it will look like in 10 or 15 years' time.

NOTE: All exercises and forms are available for download and completion at **www.growingabusinessinireland.com**.

A MISSION STATEMENT FOR YOUR BUSINESS

The mission statement sets out the reason why the business exists – what it aims to achieve, why it does what it does. It defines what the business does.

The challenge is to define what the business does in sufficiently narrow terms to provide a focus and yet, at the same time, in sufficiently broad terms to allow the business to grow. It should capture the essence of your idea and how it distinguishes you from your competitors.

For example, your mission statement might be:

"We will provide general accountancy and financial-based advisory services to clients in knowledge-based industries, such as software and telecommunications. Our service will be characterised by a high level of use and awareness of modern accounting and information technology".

Start developing the mission statement for your own business by answering these questions:

- What is the purpose of your company?
- Why does the business exist?
- What is the company about?

It is important to think carefully about your mission statement because it defines the core of the business and it strongly influences the direction of the company. It is a critical determining factor of the strategy of the business.

For example, Amazon.com's mission statement did not simply define the company as an online retailer of books, although the business started out doing that – and is still (justifiably) famous for it. Instead:

Amazon is not a book company, that's not what the brand is about. Amazon stands for a fantastic shopping experience, a different way of buying anything. Our focus now and in the future will be to provide the best online shopping experience. We want to be the place where you can find, discover or buy anything online."
ROBIN TERRELL, MANAGING DIRECTOR, AMAZON.CO.UK, IN *DIRECTOR* MAGAZINE, JULY 2002

This broader scope has allowed Amazon to branch naturally into selling videos and computer games and all the other things it now sells – and allows it diversify even further, profitably satisfying other needs among the same customers, while still remaining within the terms of its mission statement.

Use the exercise below to help you write a mission statement for your business.

**EXERCISE
A MISSION STATEMENT FOR YOUR BUSINESSS**

Write a mission statement for your business.

A Company carrying on an Undertaking of Great Advantage, but no one to know what it is.

Company prospectus at the time of the SouthS ea Bubble (1711)

To do really cool things in the field of computer communications and make a buck at it.

Mission statement of software firm, Galacticomm, quoted in Inc, 1994

Start small
Think big
Phase in
Grow fast

Baltimore
Technologies
motto

SETTING TARGETS

Defining targets — your "destination" — is the next step in deciding where you want to go. Try the exercise below.

Don't be concerned if you cannot complete the exercise in the level of detail suggested. It may be a little too early in the thinking process for you to be able to do this. The purpose now is to give you a sense of direction – you can fill in the gaps in later exercises as you work through the remaining sections of the workbook.

Every year, you should set yourself targets for the next year, keeping in mind your 10-year plan, which sets out the direction of your business.

Using a road map analogy, the 10-year plan is your destination; the one-year plans are the turns (right, left, straight, short cut, scenic route, stop-over, break for coffee, etc.) that you take on the way. And, just as on a journey by road, you need to check your direction on a regular basis to see whether your plans need adjustment.

EXERCISE
DEFINING TARGETS

What large ambitions — "Big, hairy, audacious goals" in management-speak — do you have for your business?
What are your overall targets:

> For year 1?

> For year 5?

> For year 10?

Can you set more detailed targets for your business' performance?

FINANCIAL

	Next year	Next year + 1	Next year + 2
Sales			
Gross profit			
Net profit			
Your own salary			
Total promoters/ management team remuneration			

CUSTOMERS

	Next year	Next year + 1	Next year + 2
Number of customers			
Average purchase per customer			
Average purchase per customer — units of product/service			

NOTE: All exercises and forms are available for download and completion at **www.growingabusinessinireland.com**.

EXERCISE
DEFINING TARGETS (CONT'D)

PRODUCTS/SERVICES (each of the business' top three products/services)

	Next year	Next year + 1	Next year + 2
Percentage of total sales accounted for by:			
> Product/service 1			
> Product/service 2			
> Product/service 3			
Number of products made/ hours of services supplied for:			
> Product/service 1			
> Product/service 2			
> Product/service 3			
Average cost of each unit of product made/cost of service provided per hour for:			
> Product/service 1			
> Product/service 2			
> Product/service 3			

ASSETS AND LIABILITIES

	Next year	Next year + 1	Next year + 2
Fixed assets			
Cash			
Stock on hand			
Money due by customers			
Money due to suppliers			
Total Working Capital			
Less Borrowings			
Total Net Worth of Business			
Equity contributed by promoters and management team			
External equity			
(External equity as a % of total equity)			
Profits retained			
Total Shareholders' Funds			

OTHER MEASURES

	Next year	Next year + 1	Next year + 2
Number of staff (including promoters and management team)			
New products/services			
Percentage of total sales accounted for by new products in first year			
New customers won			
Percentage of total sales accounted for by new customers in first year			

EXERCISE
DEFINING TARGETS (CONT'D)

What new customer types can you reach:
> With your existing products/services?
> With new products/services?

What new products/services will you introduce?
When?
What stage are they at now?
What market demand do you expect for each?
What competitive reaction to do expect for each?

Which of the following factors are important to the market? For each factor that is important to the market, what targets will you set for improvement and how will you reach them?

	Importance to market	Target for improvement	Method of improvement
Product features (specify what these are)			
Quality of products			
Range of products			
Customer service			
Marketing			
Price			
Location			
Delivery			
Image			
Other (specify what these are)			

Do you expect important changes in these factors?
If "Yes", what are these changes?
How can you capitalise on them?

How will you measure the success of your business in the future?

There is no "Try" - only "Do" and "Do not".

JODA,
Star Wars

NEXT STEPS

At this stage, you have a good sense of your business' future direction. Not all the details have been decided yet – it's far too early in the process for that – but you have begun the process and are making progress. You are probably excited about the prospect of growth.

But before you go anywhere, it's time to check your starting point – to make sure that your destination is reachable from where you are now.

Section 2:
Where Are You Now?

Strategy and business planning are seen by many business people as something rarified, appropriate for multinationals that can afford to employ teams of high-powered MBAs in Strategic Planning Units at their corporate headquarters, but not related to the needs of ordinary small and medium-sized businesses. Nothing could be further from the truth.

Certainly it is true that most SMEs cannot afford to employ even a single MBA, let alone a team. Few have "corporate headquarters", and fewer still have "Strategic Planning Units". But strategy is just as relevant to SMEs as it is to multinationals - it's just that SMEs are not used to formulating strategy in anything other than the most informal way.

After all, if you don't have a strategy for your business, how do you know what to do? When to do it? What not to do? Whether you are doing the right thing? Even, why do you have a business at all?

As an owner/manager, you know the answers to these questions, even if you have never taken the trouble to articulate them, let alone write them down on paper. Your business is prospering, you are looking towards growth - you must be doing something right.

This section of the **Growing Your Own Business** workbook is designed to help you and your management team to build a strategy for your business, one that you can confidently implement - and adapt as necessary as the business environment in which you operate changes.

"Strategy" consists of answering three questions, which are really quite simple:

- Where are you now?
- Where do you want to be?
- How do you get there?

We have already looked at the second. It's the first question that we will consider in this section of the workbook. We will look at the last in the third section.

OBJECTIVE

- To identify the issues involved in developing strategy

[Captain Woodrow F] Call ignored him, trying to think of some way to salvage the trip. Though he had always been a careful planner, life on the frontier had long ago convinced him of the fragility of plans.
The truth was, most plans did fail, to one degree or another, for one reason or another. He had survived as a [Texas] Ranger because he was quick to respond to what he had actually found, not because his planning was infallible.

LARRY MCMURTRY, *Lonesome Dove*, **published by Pocket Books, New York, 1985**

OBJECTIVE
- To analyse and understand the current position of the business

This is a time to take stock of your business achievements, your resources and current market position, before you raise your eyes to the horizon and the future.

EXERCISE
HOW HAS YOUR BUSINESS DONE SO FAR?

FINANCIAL	Last year	Previous year
Sales		
Gross profit		
Net profit		
Your own salary		
Total promoters/management team remuneration		

CUSTOMERS	Last year	Previous year
Number of customers		
Average purchase per customer		
Average purchase per customer - units of product/service		

PRODUCTS/SERVICES	Last year	Previous year

Percentage of total sales accounted for by each of the business'
top three products/services:
> Product/service 1
> Product/service 2
> Product/service 3

Number of products made/hours of services supplied for each of the
business' top three products/services:
> Product/service 1
> Product/service 2
> Product/service 3

Average cost of each unit of product made/cost of service provided per
hourfor each of the business' top three products/services:
> Product/service 1
> Product/service 2
> Product/service 3

ASSETS AND LIABILITIES	Last year
Previous year	
Fixed assets	
Cash	
Stock on hand	
Money due by customers	
Money due to suppliers	
Total Working Capital	
Less Borrowings	
Total Net Worth of Business	
Equity contributed by promoters and management team	
External equity	
(External equity as a % of total equity)	
Profits retained	
Total Shareholders' Funds	

OTHER MEASURES   Last year   Previous year

Number of staff (including promoters and management team)

New products/services introduced

Percentage of total sales accounted for by new products in first year

New customers won

Percentage of total sales accounted for by new customers in first year

Can you break down your sales:

By Product/service?

Product/Service Sales last year   Past growth: Good/poor? Margin last year?   Prospects: Good/poor?

By Customer type?

Customer type   Sales last year   Past growth: Good/poor? Margin last year?   Prospects: Good/poor?

By Region?

Region   Sales last year   Past growth: Good/poor? Margin last year?   Prospects: Good/poor?

On a scale of 1 to 10 (10 being very important or good performance), which of the following factors are important in your market and how is your business performing with regard to them?

                                    Importance in market   Performance of business

Product features (specify what these are)

Quality of products

Range of products

Customer service

Marketing

Price

Location

Delivery

Image

Other (specify what these are)

Why do your customers buy from you? How do you know this?

Are you capable of meeting quick changes in demand?

Are your suppliers able to help you to meet sudden changes in demand?

Are you dependent on one major supplier for any of your top three products/services?

Are you dependent on one major customer for sales of any of your top three products/services?

How do you keep informed of new developments on your industry?

How do you implement those new developments?

Are you developing new products/services?

How do the promoters and management team spend their time (week/month), on average?

	NAME/TITLE:	NAME/TITLE:	NAME/TITLE:	NAME/TITLE:
	HOURS	HOURS	HOURS	HOURS
Sales				
Production				
Meeting customers				
Administration				
Doing/learning new things				
Other activities(specify what these are)				
Total				

Why is your business successful?

However you measure success, how would you measure your business on a scale of 1 to 10 (10 being very successful)?

HOW FAR TO GO?

OBJECTIVE

- To compare the business' current situation of with that desired
- To identify the size and location of any gaps

In the first section of this workbook, you looked at where you might want to take your business. In this section - in the last exercise, in particular - you identified your current starting point. What separates the two?

Is there only a small gap? If so, where's the "growth"?

If there's a big gap, is it too big to be bridged realistically?

Is your present situation so far away from your vision as to make it appear that you are talking about different businesses?

It's clearly time for a reality check. Try this exercise.

EXERCISE
A REALITY CHECK: PRESENT VS FUTURE

Look back at the exercises **Defining Targets** (page 12) and **How Has Your Business Done So Far?** (page 18), and identify the gap between your present situation (as shown by "Last Year" in the first exercise) and your future plan (as shown by "Next Year + 2" in the second exercise).

Use a scale of 1 to 10 (where 1 signifies a small gap and 10 signifies a gap that is impossible to close).

FINANCIAL	**Present situation**	**Future plan**	**Size of Gap**
Sales			
Gross profit			
Net profit			
Your own salary			
Total promoters/management team remuneration			

CUSTOMERS	**Present situation**	**Future plan**	**Size of Gap**
Number of customers			
Average purchase per customer			
Average purchase per customer - units of product/service			

PRODUCTS/SERVICES	**Present situation**	**Future plan**	**Size of Gap**
Percentage of total sales accounted for by each of the business' top three products/services:			
> Product/service 1			
> Product/service 2			
> Product/service 3			
Number of products made/hours of services supplied for each of the business' top three products/services:			
> Product/service 1			
> Product/service 2			
> Product/service 3			
Average cost of each unit of product made/cost of service provided per hourfor each of the business' top three products/services:			
> Product/service 1			
> Product/service 2			
> Product/service 3			

NOTE: All exercises and forms are available for download and completion at **www.growingabusinessinireland.com**.

ASSETS AND LIABILITIES	Present situation	Future plan	Size of Gap
Fixed assets			
Cash			
Stock on hand			
Money due by customers			
Money due to suppliers			
Total Working Capital			
Less Borrowings			
Total Net Worth of Business			
Equity contributed by promoters and management team			
External equity			
(External equity as a % of total equity)			
Profits retained			
Total Shareholders' Funds			

OTHER MEASURES	Present situation	Future plan	Size of Gap
Number of staff			
(including promoters and management team)			
New products/services introduced			
Percentage of total sales accounted for			
by new products in first year			
New customers won			
Percentage of total sales accounted for			
by new customers in first year			

	Present situation	Future plan	Size of Gap
Product features (specify what these are)			
Quality of products			
Range of products			
Customer service			
Marketing			
Price			
Location			
Delivery			
Image			
Other (specify what these are)			

Wherever the size of your gap appears as 7 or greater on the scale, you may want to revisit your initial plans and to amend them to something more achievable.

Once you have completed this exercise, you can move onto the next, and main, section of the workbook, **How Do You Get to Where You Want To Be?**.

NOTES

SECTION 3: HOW DO YOU GET TO WHERE YOU WANT TO BE?

The only way to answer the question "How do you get to where you want to be?" is through a rigorous process of business planning.

Most small and medium-sized businesses don't engage in any sort of business planning. The excuses vary - from "We don't have the time", to "It's not necessary for us, we know our market", to "Plans never work out, so there's no point".

But the reality is that, without having gone through a process of business planning, you cannot write a business plan - not one that means anything worthwhile. Without a business plan, you will have difficulty in raising external funding. Without external funding, you are unlikely to have sufficient resources to achieve any worthwhile growth (recap from the first section on what "growth" means for your business). And, more importantly, even if you are lucky enough to have sufficient resources on hand to achieve the growth you want without accessing external funds (if so, what have you been doing with all these resources up to now?), you still need to know how to apply them wisely in the pursuit of your planned future.

So, business planning is inescapable. It's not easy, but it's not rocket-science either. This section will how you how to engage in the process of business planning, using the **SPOTcheck®** assessment model to direct your efforts.

OBJECTIVE

- To understand the distinction between process and output in business planning
- To understand how to use the SPOTcheck®. assessment model
- To be able to interpret and use the results from the SPOTcheck®. assessment model
- To be able to identify immediate actions leading to business growth

OBJECTIVE
- To understand the distinction between process and output in business planning

It's the planning, not the plan, that counts.

DWIGHT D EISENHOWER

At the outset, there is a critical distinction to be drawn between the process of business planning and the output from the process, the business plan document. **This is not merely a matter of semantics, or an academic distinction.** Not drawing this distinction is arguably the reason why so few business plans are dependable and why business planning is held in low esteem by most business people.

Statistics show that most business failures are due to inadequate or non-existent business planning. And, as a result, banks, venture capitalists and enterprise support agencies the world over unanimously insist on a business plan as a pre-condition to funding. "Write a business plan" is the first message one hears on approaching such institutions.

So, why **do** businesses continue to fail? Because they "write" a business plan! They write a business plan document, without having first engaged in the process of business planning. The information included in the document has not been properly thought through, the links between the various elements have not been explored fully and the plan itself is untested. Just like writing an essay, "What I would do if I won the Lottery" is no predictor of winning millions, a business plan that has been written without any underpinning research through a process of business planning is no predictor of business success. And since banks, venture capitalists and enterprise support agencies don't know the business, they make an assumption (usually, incorrect) that the promoter/management team does - with the result that both parties are often disappointed.

Further, since most business plans received by financing or support organisations are rejected early in the process, few business plans get the kind of attention that exposes their deeper weaknesses - and fewer still benefit from the financing or support organisation's experience to help correct those weaknesses.

Therefore, this section of **Growing Your Own Business: A Workbook** starts from the premise that the most important contribution to the successful growth of a business is the commitment of its promoters and management team to a systematic process of business planning.

This systematic process of business planning need not be a long-drawn-out affair, nor need it cost a great deal. What it does require is:
- Sustained clear thinking, away from the everyday pressures of the business
- The ability to make links between different aspects of the business and to explore them fully
- The ability to understand the key questions that determine business success or failure
- A willingness to consider and explore alternatives
- A vision of, and clear commitment, to the future.

Without this, business planning - and real prospects of growth - are more likely to fail than to succeed.

Business planning is an iterative process. As a result, plans made today may change as a result of new information yet to be discovered. This section and **Section 4** are two halves of a whole, bringing together the entire process of business planning. But this section is really the key to it all - it's where you do the thinking that gets captured in a business plan document.

Now, with an understanding of the distinction between the process and the output of business planning, let's first look at the first step in the process: Assessing your business' growth potential.

ASSESSING GROWTH POTENTIAL

SPOTcheck® was developed by Oak Tree Press, to assist in assessing the growth potential of a business. The name comes from **Success POTential Check**, which explains exactly what the model does. It is **not** an assessment of the current state of the business but an assessment of the impact on the growth potential of a business of a number of factors, all clearly identified in international research studies as being critical to growth.

SPOTcheck®:

- Provides entrepreneurs with feedback on the potential for development (start-up or growth) of their business
- Provides a firm basis for identifying and specifying the training/support required to create/sustain growth
- Allows benchmarking of scores over time and between businesses.

The **SPOTcheck®** model is usually completed by an entrepreneur on their own business. It also can be completed by a consultant with a reasonable knowledge of the business on behalf of an enterprise support agency or a client. The model, which is available online (see later) consists of 16 factors, which have been identified as being critical to the development potential of a business.

The factors are:

- **Section 1**: External factors (outside business' control): 5 factors
- **Section 2**: Promoters/Management team: 1 factor
- **Section 3**: Internal factors (within business' control): 10 factors.

Each factor consists of a number of Items, which are rated on a numerical score, between 1 and 5 (the higher the number, the better the score) for their impact on the growth potential of the business.

The output from **SPOTcheck®** is:

- A graph showing overall scores for the business for Promoters/ Management Team, Internal and External Factors in aggregate, again benchmarked against similar businesses or an earlier assessment in the database
- A graph showing the scores for the business for each Factor, benchmarked against other similar businesses or an earlier assessment in the database
- A report (full or summary) that identifies strengths, weaknesses, opportunities and threats for the business.

SPOTcheck® is available online at **www.spotcheckonline.com**. The title of this page has a Voucher ID (access code) printed on it – this gives you a free **SPOTcheck®** assessment.

This section of the workbook uses **SPOTcheck®** to identify strengths, weaknesses, opportunities and threats for your business.

The following chapters suggest further analysis that will help to eliminate these weaknesses, build on your business' strengths, maximise the opportunities available to your business and avoid any threats facing it.

Note again that **SPOTcheck®** is not a "health check" of your business, nor does it measure how good your business is - it simply assesses the impact of known growth factors on your business, thus identifying the extent and incidence of growth potential within your business. It's a tool to help direct your thinking and planning - don't make the mistake of thinking that it's a "cure-all".

OBJECTIVE
- To understand how to use the SPOTcheck® assessment model

USING SPOTCHECK®

Connect to the Internet and then to **www.spotcheckonline.com**.

The first screen you will see is the entry screen:

You should now take the time to read the "Terms of Use" page (click on the appropriate links) before entering further into the **SPOTcheck®** website.

Since this is your first time to **www.spotcheckonline.com**, click on "Register". You will see this screen:

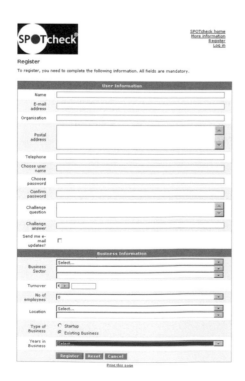

On subsequent occasions, you will use the "Log In" screen to access **SPOTcheck®**:

Registering or logging-in will take you to your Personal Account, which shows any assessments you have begun and their current state of completion:

Click on "Buy Credits", enter your Voucher ID from the title page of this workbook into the appropriate field, and click "Buy Now". This will give you credit for an assessment and return you to your Personal Account.

Click on "New Assessment" to start your assessment:

EXTERNAL FACTORS

You can tackle the **SPOTcheck®** Factors in any order you like but the first to be presented are the External Factors - those the business cannot control but which nonetheless impact on its potential for growth.

These are:

- Environment
- Market
- Customers
- Direct Competition
- Suppliers.

The assessment involves scoring your business for the impact of each Factor on its growth potential - it does **not** involve an assessment of the business as it stands.

Each Factor comprises a number of Items, each of which is to be scored.

The scoring base is as follows:

- Negative impact on growth potential - 1
- Negative impact on growth potential to neutral impact - 2
- Neutral impact on growth potential - 3
- Neutral impact on growth potential to positive impact - 4
- Positive impact on growth potential - 5.

If you feel that a particular Item is not relevant to your business, you can select the "Not Applicable" radio button instead of scoring that Item. The effect is the same as scoring "Neutral"/"3".

Information boxes (represented by the "i" symbol) provide additional information to help you score each Item. This additional information is not intended to be exhaustive, nor should you try to score each issue raised in the additional information - its purpose is simply to direct your thinking in scoring that particular Item.

Don't worry if you feel that you cannot score an Item or that you might later want to change your score. If you leave the score for an Item blank, **SPOTcheck®** will prompt you to score it before it will allow you process the data and proceed to the reporting stage. And, at any time before you process your data, you can change any score.

The navigation bar at the foot of each Factor allows you to navigate easily between factors (you can answer them in any order) and shows the number of Factors completed and their stage of completion.

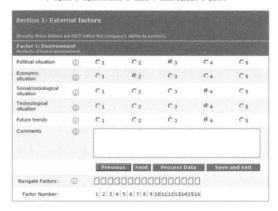

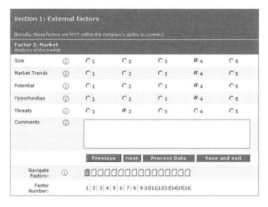

PROMOTERS/MANAGEMENT TEAM

The Factor: Promoters/Management Team is specifically isolated for assessment and later analysis because of its importance to the growth of a business. The screen looks like this:

INTERNAL FACTORS

The next screens all relate to the Internal Factors, so called because the issues in question are all within the control of the business. The screens look like this:

Again, score Promoters/Management Team in the same way as the External factors, concentrating on the impact on the growth potential of the business of each Item.

31

Ron Immink, Oak Tree Press
Remaining credits: 88

Personal Account
Buy Credits
New assessment
Log out

Assessment Questions
Growing Your Own Business

Score each item within the Factor below for their impact on the **growth potential** of your business
1 - negative 2 - negative to neutral 3 - neutral 4 - neutral to positive 5 - positive

Section 3: Internal Factors
(Broadly, these factors ARE within the company's ability to control.)

Factor 8: Marketing
Quality of marketing plan

Item	1	2	3	4	5
Strategy			●		
Marketing plan			●		
Resourcing of marketing plan		●			
Implementation of marketing plan		●			
Substantiation of sales forecasts		●			
Marketing management			●		

Comments

Previous | Next | Process Data | Save and exit

Navigate Factors:

Ron Immink, Oak Tree Press
Remaining credits: 88

Personal Account
Buy Credits
New assessment
Log out

Assessment Questions
Growing Your Own Business

Score each item within the Factor below for their impact on the **growth potential** of your business
1 - negative 2 - negative to neutral 3 - neutral 4 - neutral to positive 5 - positive

Section 3: Internal Factors
(Broadly, these factors ARE within the company's ability to control.)

Factor 9: Sales / Promotion /Channels
Analysis of sales plan

Item	1	2	3	4	5
Link with marketing strategy			●		
Organisation of sales effort				●	
Effective use of sales channels		●			
Effective use of promotion		●			
Achievement of targets		●			
Sales management			●		

Comments

Previous | Next | Process Data | Save and exit

Navigate Factors:

Ron Immink, Oak Tree Press
Remaining credits: 88

Personal Account
Buy Credits
New assessment
Log out

Assessment Questions
Growing Your Own Business

Score each item within the Factor below for their impact on the **growth potential** of your business
1 - negative 2 - negative to neutral 3 - neutral 4 - neutral to positive 5 - positive

Section 3: Internal Factors
(Broadly, these factors ARE within the company's ability to control.)

Factor 10: Products / Services
Analysis of product

Item	1	2	3	4	5
Differentiation					●
Competitiveness				●	
Stage in life-cycle			●		
Export potential/Import substitution potential			●		
Added value to customers					●
Quality					●

Comments

Previous | Next | Process Data | Save and exit

Navigate Factors:

Ron Immink, Oak Tree Press
Remaining credits: 88

Personal Account
Buy Credits
New assessment
Log out

Assessment Questions
Growing Your Own Business

Score each item within the Factor below for their impact on the **growth potential** of your business
1 - negative 2 - negative to neutral 3 - neutral 4 - neutral to positive 5 - positive

Section 3: Internal Factors
(Broadly, these factors ARE within the company's ability to control.)

Factor 11: Process
Quality of process planning

Item	1	2	3	4	5
Operational planning			●		
Equipment				●	
Efficiency				●	
Capacity				●	
Flexibility				●	
Awareness of environment			●		
Production management			●		

Comments

Previous | Next | Process Data | Save and exit

Navigate Factors:

Ron Immink, Oak Tree Press
Remaining credits: 88

Personal Account
Buy Credits
New assessment
Log out

Assessment Questions
Growing Your Own Business

Score each item within the Factor below for their impact on the **growth potential** of your business
1 - negative 2 - negative to neutral 3 - neutral 4 - neutral to positive 5 - positive

Section 3: Internal Factors
(Broadly, these factors ARE within the company's ability to control.)

Factor 12: Product development / Innovation
Quality of innovation planning

Item	1	2	3	4	5
Level of ongoing product development					●
Innovation as strategic focus					●
Involvement of staff				●	
Portfolio of ideas for product development					●
Manager(s) responsible for innovation				●	

Comments

Previous | Next | Process Data | Save and exit

Navigate Factors:

Ron Immink, Oak Tree Press
Remaining credits: 88

Personal Account
Buy Credits
New assessment
Log out

Assessment Questions
Growing Your Own Business

Score each item within the Factor below for their impact on the **growth potential** of your business
1 - negative 2 - negative to neutral 3 - neutral 4 - neutral to positive 5 - positive

Section 3: Internal Factors
(Broadly, these factors ARE within the company's ability to control.)

Factor 13: Human Resources
Quality of HRM planning

Item	1	2	3	4	5
Staffing policy			●		
Dependency on key staff			●		
Emphasis on staff development/training				●	
Motivation of staff				●	
Quality of staff					●
HRM management				●	

Comments

Previous | Next | Process Data | Save and exit

Navigate Factors:

Factor Number: 1 | 2 | 3 | 4 | 5 | 6 | 7 | 8 | 9 |10|11|12|13|14|15|16|

SPOTcheck®

Ron Immink, Oak Tree Press
Remaining credits: 88

Personal Account
Buy Credits
New assessment
Log out

Assessment Questions
Growing Your Own Business

Score each item within the Factor below for their impact on the **growth potential** of your business
1 - negative   2 - negative to neutral   3 - neutral   4 - neutral to positive   5 - positive

Section 3: Internal Factors

(Broadly, these factors ARE within the company's ability to control.)

Factor 14: Planned use of Financial Resources
Quality of financial management

		1	2	3	4	5
Financial information		○1	⦿2	○3	○4	○5
Cost control		○1	⦿2	○3	○4	○5
Cash flow management		○1	⦿2	○3	○4	○5
Bankability		○1	○2	⦿3	○4	○5
Attractiveness to private investors		○1	○2	○3	⦿4	○5
Financial strategy		○1	⦿2	○3	○4	○5
Financial management		○1	⦿2	○3	○4	○5
Comments						

[Previous] [Next] [Process Data] [Save and exit]

Navigate Factors:

SPOTcheck®

Ron Immink, Oak Tree Press
Remaining credits: 88

Personal Account
Buy Credits
New assessment
Log out

Assessment Questions
Growing Your Own Business

Score each item within the Factor below for their impact on the **growth potential** of your business
1 - negative   2 - negative to neutral   3 - neutral   4 - neutral to positive   5 - positive

Section 3: Internal Factors

(Broadly, these factors ARE within the company's ability to control.)

Factor 16: Systems & Administration
Quality of information systems and administration planning

		1	2	3	4	5
External information sources		○1	○2	○3	○4	⦿5
Internal information sources		○1	○2	⦿3	○4	○5
Appropriate systems		○1	○2	○3	⦿4	○5
Level of E-awareness		○1	○2	○3	○4	⦿5
Administration		○1	○2	○3	⦿4	○5
Learning		○1	○2	⦿3	○4	○5
Comments						

[Previous] [Next] [Process Data] [Save and exit]

Navigate Factors:

SPOTcheck®

Ron Immink, Oak Tree Press
Remaining credits: 88

Personal Account
Buy Credits
New assessment
Log out

Assessment Questions
Growing Your Own Business

Score each item within the Factor below for their impact on the **growth potential** of your business
1 - negative   2 - negative to neutral   3 - neutral   4 - neutral to positive   5 - positive

Section 3: Internal Factors

(Broadly, these factors ARE within the company's ability to control.)

Factor 15: Financial Planning
Financial Planning

		1	2	3	4	5
Working capital ratios		○1	○2	⦿3	○4	○5
Break-even analysis		○1	○2	○3	⦿4	○5
Value added		○1	○2	○3	⦿4	○5
Ratios		○1	○2	⦿3	○4	○5
Comments						

[Previous] [Next] [Process Data] [Save and exit]

Navigate Factors:

Factor Number: 1 | 2 | 3 | 4 | 5 | 6 | 7 | 8 | 9 | 10 | 11 | 12 | 13 | 14 | 15 | 16

So now try **SPOTcheck®** for yourself.

EXERCISE
SPOTCHECK® ASSESSMENT FOR YOUR BUSINESS

Log onto **www.spotcheckonline.com** and complete a **SPOTcheck®** assessment for your business.

SPOTCHECK® REPORTS

When you have completed the assessment by scoring all the Items in each of the Factors, click on the "Process data" button (**SPOTcheck®** will not allow you process data until you have scored all Items).

Then, from your Personal Account, select "View report" for this assessment. You can then choose the type of report you want from the Choose Report Type screen.

The Summary Report is shown in the following screens. It consists of a graphical overview and a table explaining the scores for each of the **SPOTcheck®** Factors. It also shows for each External Factor whether it is a Opportunity or a Threat and, for each Internal Factor (including Promoters / Management Team), whether it is a Strength or Weakness.

The Full Report (not shown) goes into more detail on the individual factors, providing scores by Item.

Ron Immink, Oak Tree Press
Remaining credits: 88

Personal Account
Buy Credits
New assessment
Log out

Choose Report Type

Assessment name: Growing Your Own Business

Report type options
- ● Summary Report
- ○ Full Report

Comparison type options
- ○ Self-assessment only
- ○ Independent assessment only
- ● Both

Compare with options
- ● Businesses from the same size bracket by employee numbers
- ○ Businesses from the same size bracket by turnover
- ○ Businesses in the same location
- ○ Businesses in the same sector
- ○ A previously entered assessment:

[select... ▼]

[Generate report]

Terms and conditions | Contact us
© www.oaktreepress.com

Ron Immink, Oak Tree Press
Remaining credits: 88

Personal Account
Buy Credits
New assessment
Log out

Summary report

Comparison Type: Both
Comparison Option: None

This report summarises your SPOTcheck assessment against your selected comparison group.
To compare your scores against another comparison group, return to the Choose Report Type page and make a new selection.
To obtain more detail on your scores, return to the Choose Report Type page and select the Full Report option (you cannot do this unless you completed a detailed SPOTcheck assessment - see the New Assessment page).

Printer friendly version

Overview graph

First, your scores for External, Promoters and Internal Factors in total, and an Overall Score, presented in graph format.

These scores are presented in percentages for ease of comparison. Scores below 50% suggest that the group of Factors (External, for example) has little impact on your business' growth potential, while the higher the score over 50%, the greater the suggested impact of the group of Factors on your business' growth potential. The Overall score gives an indication of the growth potential of your business - clearly, here, the higher the score, the better.

Assessment name: Growing Your Own Business

Summary Graphic Report:

Average for this SPOTcheck

Average for Comparison SPOTcheck

Factor graph

Next, your score for Factor is presented in graph format, giving you greater insight into the sources of growth potential within your business.

These scores are presented as numbers, with negative numbers indicating negative scores and positive numbers indicating positive scores. The scoring range on each Factor is from -30 to +30. The graph shows instantly where your business stands on each Factor, and how that Factor impacts on the growth potential of your business.

Assessment name: Growing Your Own Business

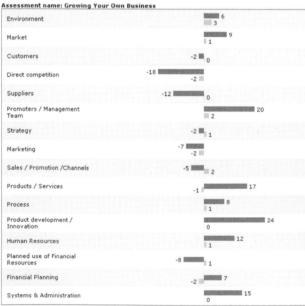

Factor Graph Legend:

Average for this SPOTcheck

Average for Comparison SPOTcheck

Factor table

This part of the report presents the same information as in the Factor graph but in table format. In addition, the table provides a SWOT analysis - in other words, it indicates whether your score for each Factor suggests a Strength, Weakness, Opportunity or Threat in that area. This is useful information for you in considering the future direction and development of your business.

Factor Number Factor Name	Score for this SPOTcheck	Average Score for Comparison Group	SWOT
External factors			
1 Environment	6	3	
2 Market	9	1	
3 Customers	-2	0	
4 Direct competition	-18	-2	Threat
5 Suppliers	-12	0	
Promoters/management team			
6 Promoters / Management Team	20	2	Strength
Internal Factors			
7 Strategy	-2	1	
8 Marketing	-7	-2	
9 Sales / Promotion /Channels	-5	2	
10 Products / Services	17	-1	Strength
11 Process	8	1	
12 Product development / Innovation	24	0	Strength
13 Human Resources	12	1	
14 Planned use of Financial Resources	-8	1	
15 Financial Planning	7	-2	
16 Systems & Administration	15	0	

For actions to help your business maximise its opportunities, avoid threats, eliminate weaknesses and build on its strengths, see www.growingabusinessinireland.com (existing businesses) / www.startingabusinessinireland.com (start-ups).

Note: SPOTcheck is an assessment tool that helps entrepreneurs identify the growth potential of their business and the areas where intervention may be required for successful growth. It is not a substitute for individual judgement and planning, and professional advice where appropriate. See Terms of Use.

Terms and conditions | Contact us
© www.oaktreepress.com

Print out the reports and study them carefully. They will be your guides through the following chapters of this workbook.

By this stage, you have an insight into your business - as it is now, and as you would like it to be. Intuitively, from the **SPOTcheck®** report, and the other exercises, you have a sense of immediate actions that you should list in order to grow your business.

List them in the exercise below.

EXERCISE
IMMEDIATE ACTIONS

For each **SPOTcheck®** Factor with a negative score, identify immediate actions that you could take to improve your business' score in this area - in other words, to provide it with greater growth potential.

FACTOR	Score	Immediate Actions
1: Environment		
2: Market		
3: Customers		
4: Direct competition		
5: Suppliers		
6: Promoters/Management Team		
7: Strategy		
8: Marketing		
9: Sales / Promotion / Channels		
10: Products / Services		
11: Process		
12: Product development / Innovation		
13: Human Resources		
14: Use of Financial Resources		
15: Financial Performance		
16: Systems & Administration		

There's no rocket science to strategy ... you're supposed to know where you are, where your competition is, what your cost position is, and where you want to go. Strategies are intellectually simple; their execution is not.
LAWRENCE A BOSSIDY, CEO, Allied-Signal

We will use the **SPOTcheck®** report as the basis for directing you through this section of the workbook.

Essentially, **Strengths** are those Internal Factors in which the business has positive scores, while **Weaknesses** derive from negative scores in the same Factors; **Opportunities** arise from positive scores in External Factors, while **Threats** come from negative scores in External Factors.

With this in mind, we can identify a range of possible immediate actions and further analysis. These are considered in the following chapters.

MOAT AND WEBS

OBJECTIVE
- To understand the business' external environment
- To understand the business' internal factors
- To understand how to develop strategy

There are two acronyms that you should bear in mind as you work through the chapters in this section of the Growing Your Own Business workbook:

- MOAT
- WEBS.

MOAT

The first acronym, MOAT, relates to External Factors. MOAT stands for **"Maximise Opportunities, while Avoiding Threats"**.

External Factors are so defined because the business has little or no control over them - few businesses have the power to control the economy or to influence significantly new legislation or to determine the scale of competition among their suppliers. These things are given. Where they have a negative impact on the growth potential of the business, often little can be done, other than to avoid them - for example, by changing processes to avoid fines under environmental legislation, or seeking new markets if existing ones are cut off and so on.

On the other side, where opportunities have been identified through **SPOTcheck®**'s External Factors, the business should seek to maximise these. For example, new

legislation may provide opportunities for new markets, new customers, new products or services - or all of the above. Think of examples in your industry.

You can visualise MOAT as a pentagon, within which your business operates. The length of each of the sides - in other words, the SPOTcheck® External Factor score for that Factor - determines both the shape and size of the pentagon. MOAT is the space in which your business has freedom to manoeuvre - it cannot operate outside the area bounded by MOAT.

WEBS

WEBS is an acronym for **"Weaknesses Eliminated, Build on Strengths"** and relates to the Internal Factors. It is more important to eliminate any weaknesses that your business may have in its potential for growth than to spend resources becoming better at what you already do well. The argument for this is based on the "weakest link" concept - that a chain always breaks at its weakest link. Strengthening the stronger links does nothing to prevent the chain breaking, while strengthening weak links allows them to bear more pressure before breaking.

The WEBS acronym also has another aspect: It visualises the **SPOTcheck®** Internal Factors, with the management team at the centre, since it lies at the heart of the organisation.

Visually, the size of the Management Team star and the length of the lines for each of the other Internal Factors represent the **SPOTcheck®** Internal Factor score for each factor.

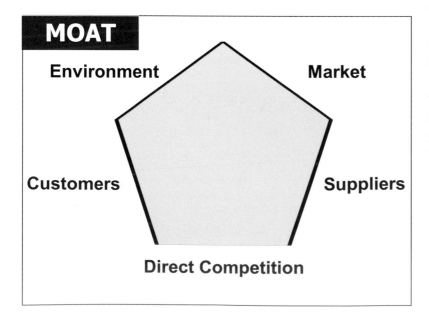

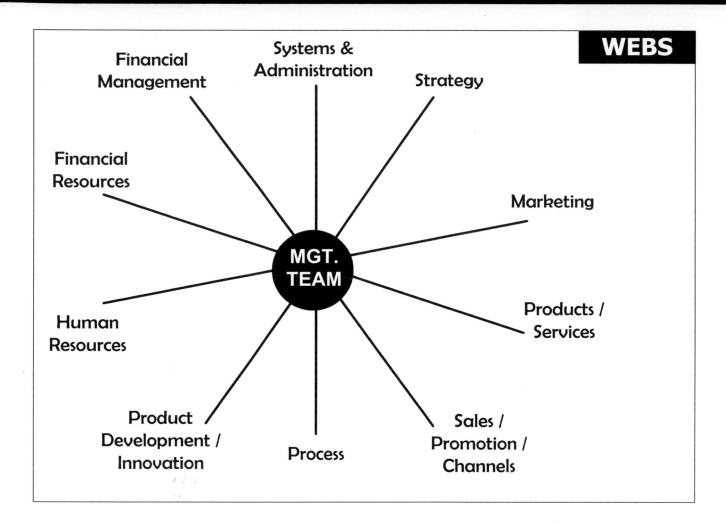

COMBINING MOAT AND WEBS

Combining MOAT and WEBS provides an immediate visual representation of the growth potential of your business:

- The bigger your MOAT, the bigger the operating space for your business and thus the greater the growth potential
- The bigger the Management team star, the greater the growth potential inherent in the team.
- The longer the WEBS lines, the greater the growth potential in the individual Internal Factors.

You may find such a visual representation helpful in grasping the concept and in seeing how **SPOTcheck®** can apply to your business.

OBJECTIVE

- To understand the impact of the business environment on the growth potential of the business
- To identify appropriate interventions to maximise opportunities and avoid threats
- To define targets, actions and the resource implications of these
- To draft text for the business plan

SPOTcheck®
Score for this Factor

IMMEDIATE ACTIONS

ANALYSIS

Unfortunately, the external environment is outside of the control of your business. Nonetheless, it will impact on your business and its growth potential, to a greater or lesser degree. Since it is outside your control, all you can do is to maximise the opportunities the external environment presents and avoid the threats it poses - hence, MOAT (maximise opportunities, while avoiding threats).

REGULATORY SITUATION

Because regulations now come from such a wide variety of sources - local, national, EU and international, depending on the markets in which you operate (or plan to operate) - it is vital that you are fully aware of what regulations may impact on your business. You should consult a solicitor experienced in your area. Use the exercise below to determine where you may need advice.

EXERCISE
REGULATORY SITUATION

	Local	National	EU	International

What regulations impact your business now?
> Environmental
> Data protection
> Product liability
> Audit/corporate governance
> Other (identify)

What regulations are likely to impact it in the near future?
> Environmental
> Data protection
> Product liability
> Audit/corporate governance
> Other (identify)

What sources of information do you have for each type of regulations?
> Environmental
> Data protection
> Product liability
> Audit/corporate governance
> Other (identify)

HEALTH & SAFETY

One of the key regulatory elements that is of increasing importance to all businesses is health and safety legislation. Not only is the legislation becoming more and more complex, it's also being enforced with increasing vigour. The UK is currently debating introducing the concept of "corporate killing" into law, under which directors of companies would be personally liable for a criminal offence in the event of the death of an employee while on the job. This would bring the responsibility for health and safety at work to new levels.

As owner/manager, it is your responsibility to be up-to-date on the law in this area as it applies to your business - and to ensure that the law is implemented appropriately throughout your business.

CORPORATE GOVERNANCE

This area is receiving increasing attention worldwide, in the wake of the Enron and other financial/accounting/business scandals. There are standards and codes of practice to be observed - only a few are mandatory, most are still voluntary. Again, make sure you are aware of developments and implement them effectively. You are at risk if you do not!

There are obvious links here to the quality and effectiveness of your management team and also to your ethics and values (see the chapter **Promoters / Management Team**).

ECONOMIC AND SOCIOLOGICAL SITUATION

Do you pray for rain or for sunshine? Some businesses follow the general economic cycles, others are anti-cyclic - for example, liquidators, who close down businesses, do best when businesses are failing in their hundreds and do very little

business in a boom. Is your business like this - or does it follow normal trends?

EXERCISE
ECONOMIC AND SOCIOLOGICAL SITUATION

Is your business now:
> Anti-cycle?
> In line with the normal economic cycle?

Could you change the cycle?
What impact would it have on the growth potential of your business?

For businesses that operate within the normal economic cycle, key indicators include:
- Cost-base
- Disposable income
- Market size
- Tax rates and burden, etc.

Use the exercise below to identify which of these are useful indicators for your business, their current impact and their trend. If none are useful to your specific situation, look for other indicators.

EXERCISE
ECONOMIC AND SOCIOLOGICAL INDICATORS

	Useful? Yes/No	Current Impact Positive/Negative	Trend Positive/Negative
Cost-base			
Disposable Income			
Market size			
Tax rates and burden			
Demographics			
Changes in family structure			
Other (specify)			

TECHNOLOGICAL SITUATION

Technology is increasingly a key factor in the success of businesses. It's important in the way businesses use technology to improve processes. But, more important is disruptive technology - profound and sudden changes in technology that have the potential to destroy your business.

For example, no travel agent 10 years ago could have thought that the Internet would destroy their intermediary role in the reservations process by allowing travellers to book their own tickets and accommodation online. Hence the increasing importance of product innovation and development as a strategic line of defence - see the chapter on **Product Development/ Innovation**.

FUTURE TRENDS

Because of the risks that other people's innovation poses (ignoring entirely the threat posed by disruptive technology), you need not only to be aware of the trends in your market area (technology, competition, trade regulations, etc.) but also have a sense of the general direction in which the world is developing. Train yourself to watch trends.

In the same way that you visualised the future of your business in **Section 1**, now visualise the future within which your business will operate.

OUTPUT

Now that you have analysed the impact of the **SPOTcheck®** External Factor: Environment on the growth potential of your business, collate the results of your analysis. You will find this useful in **Section 4: Business Planning**.

EXERCISE
IMPACT OF DEVELOPMENTS

Consider the impact on the future of your business of:
> The use of drugs for specific purposes (memory enhancers, warfare, work)
> Development of genetic engineering
> The role of computers, and telecommunications in our society
> The ability to connect with anyone in the world
> Merging of biology, cybernetics, nano-technology, computers, genetics, telecommunication into new products
> The impact of the Internet on almost every aspect of our lives, in both personal and business contexts
> The mix of technology and ancient wisdom/different cultures
> Virtual reality.

EXERCISE
PREDICTING THE FUTURE

(Be as visual as possible. Complete the exercise as if describing a photograph or a painting or a movie of the future.)

What will Ireland look like in 2010 - or even in 2025?
Where will your business fit?
What should you be doing to prepare?

OUTPUT	Planning(now)	ThisYear	NextYear	YearAfter
TARGETS				
ACTIONS				
RESOURCE IMPLICATIONS				
Time				
Money				
People				
Other				

OUTPUT TO BUSINESS PLAN	
Text	Description of environment - threats and opportunities
Evidence	Supporting analyses
Numbers	Resource implications - as above

SPOTcheck®
Score for this Factor

IMMEDIATE ACTIONS

ANALYSIS

No market, no business - never mind growth! So knowing as much as you can about your market is essential. Growth will probably mean entering new markets as well exploiting current markets more deeply.

You need to complete the exercises that follow for each product, service or revenue stream that is key to your business or is likely to be so in the future.

MARKET RESEARCH

Ongoing market research and a well-developed information system have been identified by international research as key success factors. Information is power. The strategic choices you make should be based on solid market information. Try this exercise.

If this information is not available, you need to invest time and money in:

- Basic market research to assess the real potential and the future direction of your present and future markets
- An information system - see **Systems & Administration**.

MARKET TRENDS

Where are the markets for your products/services/revenue streams going? These market trends will

---

EXERCISE
MARKET RESEARCH

Does your (ongoing) market research cover:

Market size?	☐ Yes ☐ No
Market structure?	☐ Yes ☐ No
Market trends?	☐ Yes ☐ No
Market potential?	☐ Yes ☐ No
Market share?	☐ Yes ☐ No
Market stability/volatility?	☐ Yes ☐ No
Competitor activity?	☐ Yes ☐ No
Competitor prices?	☐ Yes ☐ No
Competitor products/services?	☐ Yes ☐ No
User attitudes/behaviour?	☐ Yes ☐ No
Government factors?	☐ Yes ☐ No
Economic factors?	☐ Yes ☐ No
Demographic factors?	☐ Yes ☐ No
Future trends:	
> Economic?	☐ Yes ☐ No
> Technological?	☐ Yes ☐ No
> Cultural?	☐ Yes ☐ No
> In your industry?	☐ Yes ☐ No

---

determine the direction of your business. Use the exercise on the next page to help you to identify these trends.

Market stability, or volatility, is a key issue. Stable markets, by definition, have low growth potential. Volatile markets, on the other hand, provide ample opportunities for growth - but also for failure, sometimes very sudden failure.

OBJECTIVE

- To understand the impact of the market on the growth potential of the business
- To identify appropriate interventions to maximise opportunities and avoid threats
- To define targets, actions and the resource implications of these
- To draft text for the business plan

Market research consists of attacking the facts at the point of greatest astonishment.

SYLVIA GREEN

We are the tenth largest brewer in the United States. Do you know what that means? We have one two-hundredth of the beer market. That's miniscule. Twelve years of busting my ass, and we've gone from nothing to infinitesmal. If I'm lucky, I'll go another 12 years and get to be small.

JIM KOCH, founder and CEO of Boston Beer Company, maker of *Samuel Adams* beer

EXERCISE
MARKET TRENDS

Describe fully the main trends in your market(s)and how they impact your business?

At what stage of the lifecycle is the market?

> Start-up?

> Growth?

> Maturity?

> Decline?

What does this stage of life-cycle mean to your business?

EXERCISE
SEGMENTS/NICHES

What segments/niches do you market to?

What segments/niches do you control?

What segments/niches could you control?

How?

What other segments/niches could you market to?

Could you control these?

How?

As a growing business, with (probably) limited resources, you need to look for specific market segments and/or niches that will give you maximum return. Modern marketing theory suggests that "controlling your niche" is more important than overall market share.

OUTPUT

Now that you have analysed the impact of the **SPOTcheck®** External Factor: Market on the growth potential of your business, collate the results of your analysis. You will find this useful in **Section 4: Business Planning**.

OUTPUT	Planning(now)	ThisYear	NextYear	YearAfter
TARGETS				
ACTIONS				
RESOURCE IMPLICATIONS				
Time				
Money				
People				
Other				
OUTPUT TO BUSINESS PLAN				
Text	Description of market; Segments/niches to control			
Evidence	Market research results			
Numbers	Resource implications - as above			

NOTE: All exercises and forms are available for download and completion at **www.growingabusinessinireland.com**.

SPOTcheck®
Score for this Factor

IMMEDIATE ACTIONS

| |
| |
| |
| |
| |

ANALYSIS

To grow your business in terms of sales volume, you can:

- Sell more of your existing products, services or revenue streams to existing customers
- Sell new products, services or revenue streams to existing customers
- Find new customers and sell existing products, services or revenue streams to them
- Find new customers and sell new products, services or revenue streams to them.

Obviously, the last two methods are more difficult than the first two.

CUSTOMER RETENTION

However, your starting point should be to secure the sale of existing products, services or revenue streams to existing customers - to make sure that you retain these customers and generate repeat sales from them. In most companies, too much focus is placed on new sales, rather than sales retention. To see the importance of repeat sales, complete the exercise on the life-time value of the customer.

And don't overlook the importance of

EXERCISE
THE LIFE-TIME VALUE OF A CUSTOMER

Average sale value per customer _____
 multiplied by
Number of sales per year per customer _____
Total sales value per year per customer _____
 multiplied by
Number of years during which
 the customer buys from you _____
Gross lifetime sales value per customer _____

---

referrals - an existing customer who refers a potential customer to your business. The car manufacturer Lexus estimates that the lifetime referral value of a single customer is $600,000 (about 10 times the value of the original sale to that customer). Think about how powerful referrals could be in the context of your sales forecasts - see the chapter on **Sales / Promotion / Channels**.

CUSTOMER ANALYSIS

Hence the importance of knowing your customers. We presume you know your customers already. Use the exercise on the next page to check how well you know them.

OBJECTIVE
- To understand the impact of customers on the growth potential of the business
- To identify appropriate interventions to maximise opportunities and avoid threats
- To define targets, actions and the resource implications of these
- To draft text for the business plan

*The four advantages of loyal customers:
They buy more
They cheaper to service
They bring new customers
They don't buy on price.*

MURRAY RAPHAEL

EXERCISE
YOUR CUSTOMERS

	Current	Planned

Your customers/target groups:
Who are they?
Which are the most promising?
Where are they located?
How do they spend their time?
How do they spend their money?
Where do they spend their money?
How are they organised?
Where do they socialise?
What issues are important to them?
What do they read?
What do they watch on TV?
What do they listen to on radio?
Who forms their opinions?
Where do they buy products/services similar to yours?

EXERCISE
CUSTOMERS' BUYING DECISIONS

How much information do your customers collect before buying?
How much time is spent on the selecting the right item to buy?
Is it a once-off buy or a regular purchase?
Who is involved in making the buying decision?
> Customer only?
> Customer and spouse/partner or customer and business colleagues?
> Customer and family?
> Customer and outsiders?
Is buying based on an impulse?
How quickly do customers want delivery of your product/service after making the purchase?
Does your product need service or maintenance?
If so, can this be sold to the customer at the time of buying your product?
How long will the customer use your product?
Is your customers' buying decision process changing?
Do you need to adjust?
What are the five most important features of your product/service for the customer's buying decision?

EXERCISE
KEY CUSTOMER DEPENDENCIES

What % of your turnover is dependent on your top 3 key customers? _____%
Do you think that is too high?
What % of your total sales do you expect from these customers
 in the next 5 years?   _____%
What happens if these customers disappear overnight?
What alternatives do you have in place?

As well as identifying the exact needs and wants of your customers, it is also important to identify how the customer makes a buying decision. Use the next exercise to help you identify this process.

WHO ARE YOUR KEY CUSTOMERS AND WHY?

Key customers may be key to your business for reasons other than just sales, such as:
• Their willingness to share technology
• Their willingness to share information
• They are a route to future markets
• They are potential strategic partners.

DEPENDENCY ON KEY CUSTOMERS

Too much dependency on key customers is not healthy. Have you any potentially dangerous dependencies?

As a final review of your customers, try the **Customer-Base Analysis** exercise on the next page.

YOUR BUSINESS' REPUTATION WITH CUSTOMERS

To determine your strategy-particularly brand strategy, you need to know how your customers perceive your business and/or your products/services/revenue streams. Ask them. Record their perceptions in the exercise below.

EXERCISE
CUSTOMER PERCEPTIONS

Survey or talk to your customers.
Summarise the results.

EXERCISE
CUSTOMER-BASE ANALYSIS

First, analyse your whole customer base to identify the 20% of customers that make up 80% of sales/profits. Then for each of these customers, consider their:

> Future sales potential

> Future potential as partners/allies

> Future potential problems.

CUSTOMERS	% Sales	Potential for:		
		Sales	Partnership/Alliance	Problems
1.				
2.				
3.				
4.				
5.				
Total				

INTERNATIONAL CUSTOMERS

The Irish market alone is unlikely to facilitate the growth of your company. You will have to look at the international market to achieve significant growth. The obvious starting point is your current international customers, if any, who can be potential strategic partners for entry into those markets and a useful source of information.

EXERCISE
INTERNATIONAL CUSTOMERS

Who are your current international customers?

What % of your turnover do they make up?

How did you gain these customers?

Could you gain more in the same way?

How much do you want grow internationally?

Use the exercise to help you think through the implications of exporting. Clearly, there are links between this exercise and the later chapters on **Marketing** and **Sales / Promotion / Channels**. Revisit your answers to the exercise when you have read these later chapters.

EXERCISE
EXPORTING

How specific are your plans for exporting?

Are they an integral part of your business plan and strategy for the business?

Which products/services/revenue streams do you want to export?

Which countries do you want to export to and in which order of priority?

What are your target market segments within the market?

Have you done desk research on your export markets?

Have you actually visited the countries involved? (Holiday visits don't count!)

Do you have sales experience in your proposed export markets?

Do you have the language skills needed?

Have you organised your administration for foreign payments and customs/excise regulations?

Are you familiar with the regulations relating to your products/services in your export markets?

Does your product or service need adjustment? For example, for safety, environment, quality, packaging, taste, fashion, culture or language?

Is your price, after calculation of the extra costs involved in exporting, still competitive?

What are your turnover targets: per country, per market, per segment?

Do you have enough time available to build and develop the export market?

Who will be responsible for marketing and sales abroad?

Is your organisation, from telephonist to after sales, ready and prepared for export and dealing internationally?

Can your business cope with the demands of foreign markets: Delivery times, transport, quantities?

Which channels are you planning to use in your export markets?

Do you have the right promotion and instruction materials?

Are your term and conditions, contracts, quotes, etc. translated and adjusted to your export markets?

OUTPUT

Now that you have analysed the impact of the **SPOTcheck®** External Factor: Customers on the growth potential of your business, collate the results of your analysis. You will find this useful in **Section 4: Business Planning**.

OUTPUT	Planning(now)	ThisYear	NextYear	YearAfter
TARGETS				
ACTIONS				
RESOURCE IMPLICATIONS				
Time				
Money				
People				
Other				
OUTPUT TO BUSINESS PLAN				
Text	Customer analysis; Description of current reputation among customers			
Evidence	Market research			
Numbers	Resource implications - as above			

NOTE: All exercises and forms are available for download and completion at **www.growingabusinessinireland.com**.

NOTES

SPOTcheck®
Score for this Factor

IMMEDIATE ACTIONS

OBJECTIVE
- To understand the impact of direct competition on the growth potential of the business
- To identify appropriate interventions to maximise opportunities and avoid threats
- To define targets, actions and the resource implications of these
- To draft text for the business plan

ANALYSIS

To assess the competitiveness of your business you need a benchmark. The most obvious benchmark is your competitors. Study them and score how they are performing on criteria that are important to the market and customers (see your earlier research). Try to identify areas in which:

- Your business is stronger
- Your business is weaker
- You can learn from your competitors
- Your business needs to improve
- Your competitors are developing and which you are ignoring (why?).

COMPETITORS

You need to establish a competitive advantage over your competitors - price, quality, service or some other area of importance to your customers. This competitive advantage is of major strategic importance, as your competitors (and hopefully your customers) will react most directly to your growth strategy.

The modern view of competitiveness is based on cost-effectiveness and on designing the most competitive business model. But, first, you need to know who your competitors are. You probably already do - use the exercise below to check how well you know them.

EXERCISE
COMPETITORS

	Current	Planned
What are the alternatives to your products/services?		
Who makes/sells these alternatives?		
Among these, who are your main competitors?		
What range of products/services do they have?		
What kind of choices do they offer customers?		
How broad is their range?		
What are their target groups?		
What are their future prospects?		
What are they good at and what are they not so good at?		
What implications do your competitors have for your products/services?		

PRICE COMPETITIVENESS

The unit selling price of your products, services and revenue streams is a critical determinant of your company's bottom line. All other things being equal, the more you can charge, the more you make in margin.

To determine your room to manoeuvre in pricing, you need to know how your price is calculated:

- **Cost plus** - you take the cost of producing the product (or delivering a service) and add a margin - and hope this fits with customers' willingness/ability to pay
- **Market minus** - you take the price customers are willing/able to pay - and produce for less than this.

The more unique you make your product, the easier it is to price on cost plus. See the chapters on **Products/Services** and on **Process**.

Then you need to look at your competitors' pricing, to see where your pricing falls in relation to theirs.

Use the exercise on the next page on price manoeuvrabaility to guide you here.

The answers to these questions will inform your generic strategic direction. Are you going to compete on price or will you compete on value? A price-competitive strategy is high-risk, as the resulting low margins leave you little profit to invest in product or process innovation. In addition, you are exposed to a competitor with "deep pockets" who can afford to undercut your prices for as long as it takes to put you out of business. Can you sustain competing on price for the long-term? Competing on value is generally regarded as a better strategy - though it does require considerable thought to defining "value" - especially since the definition is from the customer's viewpoint.

The next part of this chapter begins to explore value.

PRODUCT/SERVICE COMPARISON

Compare your products and services against those of your competitors, using the exercise on the next page

INTENSITY OF COMPETITIVE BEHAVIOUR

The intensity of the competition you face is mainly dependent on the structure of the market.

How many alternatives are there to your product or service?

How many companies are active in the same market?

Is it easy to set up a business in the market?

The intensity is another determinant of your main strategic direction. The competitive forces in the market, combined with the resources available to you, will decide whether your competitive strategy will be to go all out for full-blown war or to snipe at your competitors in a series of guerrilla attacks. Alternatively, you might decide to consolidate your market segments and defend rather than attack.

You can sometimes sidestep the intensity of competition by creating barriers that make it difficult for competitors to compete. The use of networks in a niche market, protection of intellectual property rights though patents, and branding are all examples of competitive barriers.

As competitive behaviour is not a static situation (it's a jungle out there!) you need to be mindful of trends in the future and any expected change in intensity. This requires ongoing market research..

Competition makes life turbulent and uncertain. Competition almost always eats into profits. Worse, you can lose at competition.

CHARLES MANN

EXERCISE
PRICE MANOEUVRABILITY

For each product/service/revenue stream, identify:

Product/service/revenue stream	Your cost of production/delivery	Your selling price	Your competitors' lowest selling price (for the same/ similar product)	Your competitors' highest selling price (for the same/ similar product)
1.				
2.				
3.				
4.				
5.				

Now plot this information on a chart, like so:

P/S/RS																
1		○					●	◇		◆						
2			○				◇	●	◆							
3				◇	○	◆	●									
	1	2	3	4	5	6	7	8	9	10	11	12	13	14	15	Cost/Price

Legend: ○ Your own cost ● Your own selling price
◇ Lowest competitor selling price ◆ Highest competitor selling price.

Now try it with your own information.

P/S/RS																
1																
2																
3																
4																
5																
6																
7																
8																
	1	2	3	4	5	6	7	8	9	10	11	12	13	14	15	Cost/Price

EXERCISE
PRODUCT/SERVICE COMPARISON

For each of your products/services, take the five features that your customers identify as being most important to them and decide whether your product is better (+), equal (=) or not as good (-) when compared to your three closest direct competitors' same/similar products/services.

FEATURE   **Product/Service:**

	Competitor 1:			Competitor 2:			Competitor 3:		
	Better	Same	Not as good	Better	Same	Not as good	Better	Same	Not as good
1:									
2:									
3:									
4:									
5:									

What implications does this analysis have for your product/service?

Where can you compete most strongly?

Now that you have analysed the impact of the **SPOTcheck®** External Factor: Direct Competition on the growth potential of your business, collate the results of your analysis. You will find this useful in **Section 4: Business Planning.**

OUTPUT	Planning(now)	ThisYear	NextYear	YearAfter
TARGETS				
ACTIONS				
RESOURCE IMPLICATIONS				
Time				
Money				
People				
Other				

OUTPUT TO BUSINESS PLAN	
Text	Analysis of competition, present and planned; Product/service analysis vs competitors; Pricing strategy
Evidence	Market research
Numbers	Resource implications - as above

NOTES

SPOTcheck®
Score for this Factor

IMMEDIATE ACTIONS

ANALYSIS

If you have been in business for some time, you have an extensive network of suppliers in place. Some are critical to your operation - they supply key materials or parts or services. Others are important, but could be replaced albeit with a little disruption. Some are insignificant and can be replaced almost instantly. Despite this, all your suppliers are part of your network and thus important.

KEY SUPPLIERS

Now that you are thinking about growth, your key suppliers may not be the right ones either to go forward with you or to move you forward. So you need to evaluate all your key supplier relationships, perhaps look to new ones and determine where the future lies.

You need to do these exercises for each key product, service or revenue stream that is, or is likely to be in future, critical to your business.

EXERCISE
KEY SUPPLIERS

Who are your existing key suppliers?

What are their strengths?

What are their weaknesses?

Who are the alternatives to these suppliers?

What are the alternatives' strengths?

What are the alternatives' weaknesses?

Where does the advantage lie between current and alternative suppliers:

> Now?

> In the future, as your business grows?

First identify your key suppliers and their characteristsics in the exercise opposite. Then analyse your entire supplier-base in the exercise on the next page.

OBJECTIVE

- To understand the impact of suppliers on the growth potential of the business
- To identify appropriate interventions to maximise opportunities and avoid threats
- To define targets, actions and the resource implications of these
- To draft text for the business plan

NOTE: All exercises and forms are available for download and completion at **www.growingabusinessinireland.com**.

EXERCISE
SUPPLIER-BASE ANALYSIS

Analyse your whole supplier-base to identify:
> The 20% that make up 80% of purchases/profits
> Future supplier/purchases potential
> Future potential partners/alliances
> Possible problems

SUPPLIERS	% Purchases	Potential for:		
		Purchases	Partnership/Alliance	Problems
1.				
2.				
3.				
4.				
5.				
Total				

DEPENDENCY ON KEY SUPPLIERS

In the same way that you do not want to be too dependent on a few key customers, you do not want to be too dependent on a few key suppliers. Do you have "critical" suppliers? How critical are they?

EXERCISE
KEY SUPPLIER DEPENDENCIES

How dependent are you on key suppliers?
What happens if a key supplier disappears overnight?
What alternatives have you in place?

OUTSOURCING

Outsourcing is a technique whereby parts of the business are handled by specialists outside the business. Common examples of outsourcing include:

- Sub-contractors for specific tasks
- Consultants for professional advice
- Freelancers to help with peak workloads.

But a more modern view of outsourcing is based on cost-effectiveness and designing the most competitive business model.

There are many activities that make up a business' process from product conception to final delivery to customer. In only a few of these can the business expect to enjoy a competitive advantage over other similar businesses. For example, you may be a brilliant designer, but are all your administration systems world-class too? So, increasingly, businesses are identifying parts of their process that can be outsourced to specialists - the accounting function, debt collection, product design, etc. Many of these functions, though not all, are administrative in nature - some businesses even contract out their marketing. The advantages lie in a saving on resources that would otherwise be committed to non-core activities.

As you work through your business process (see the chapter on **Process**), consider where outsourcing could benefit your business. Another reason for considering outsourcing is scale. Perhaps your business plans to manufacture and sell a new form of car tyre. Your skills lie in selling and you already have a well-established network of potential sales outlets within the motor industry. Your market research identifies a minimum investment of

€/£10 million for the factory and equipment needed to make your new tyre - well beyond your capacity to finance. By outsourcing the manufacturing under licence to a manufacturer with spare capacity, you might be able to reduce your investment significantly, and free your time to concentrate on what you do best - selling.

ASSESSING NEW SUPPLIERS

Your purchasing is likely to affect the core of your product or service and is a determinant of the quality of your product or service. Therefore, you need to keep up-to-date on developments on the purchasing front, not only from a pricing perspective, but also from a technology perspective.

Especially where a supplier is critical to your process, it is important that you conduct some form of assessment before taking on the supplier. Consider the points in the exercise below. Depending on how critical the product or service is to your business, the weight that you might assign to each of the different points changes. For some services, financial strength may be more important than price. IT is an example, where you want your IT supplier to remain in business for at least as long as you expect to run the hardware/ software combination they supply - on the other hand, a stationer that supplies brand names products can easily be replaced, and so price (or perhaps service) may be the determining factor here. In other cases, using high profile brand name parts may rub off some of the supplier's profile onto your own product - for example, many PC manufacturers use "Intel Inside" stickers on their products to distinguish them from other products using other types of chips.

EXERCISE OUTSOURCING

Which of your business functions could be outsourced?
Why?
How?
Which are outsourced now?
With what result?
Which cannot be outsourced?
Why not?

EXERCISE NEW SUPPLIER ASSESSMENT

For each new supplier, consider the following:
Organisation:
> Size
> Capacity
> Financial strength
> Innovation
> Reputation
> Branding
> Values
> E-capability
> Potential partner

Service:
> Delivery times
> Ease of ordering
> Technical assistance available
> Complaints handling
> Pro-active response to queries

Product/service:
> Price
> Credit terms
> Quality
> Warranty
> Packaging.

AVAILABILITY OF CREDIT FACILITIES

Credit facilities offered by your suppliers are often overlooked, but can be particularly important in a growth situation when your own cash-flow may be strained.

Your credit facilities with your suppliers should be at least as good as the credit terms you give your customers. However, you may need to balance monetary considerations against considerations such as:

- Strategic importance
- Courtesy and ethics
- Reliability and other factors.

The exercise you have just completed on New Supplier Assessment may help you balance such considerations.

OUTPUT

Now that you have analysed the impact of the **SPOTcheck®** External Factor: Suppliers on the growth potential of your business, collate the results of your analysis. You will find this useful in **Section 4: Business Planning.**

OUTPUT	Planning(now)	ThisYear	NextYear	YearAfter
TARGETS				
ACTIONS				
RESOURCE IMPLICATIONS				
Time				
Money				
People				
Other				
OUTPUT TO BUSINESS PLAN				
Text	Analysis of suppliers, present and planned			
Evidence	Market research			
Numbers	Resource implications - as above; Credit terms agreed with suppliers			

NOTE: All exercises and forms are available for download and completion at **www.growingabusinessinireland.com**.

The five chapters you have just completed cover the **SPOTcheck®** External Factors: Environment, Market, Customers, Direct Competition and Suppliers.

These factors are largely outside the control of your business and so you must accept them as they are. However, your response to them should be to **"Maximise Opportunities, Avoid Threats"** - hence, **MOAT.**

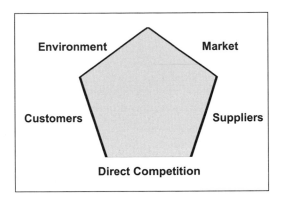

Think of these factors visually as the moat that surrounded and defended a medieval castle. Within the moat was a safe area, behind which the inhabitants could take shelter in times of attack. Although medieval moats were constructed close to the castle walls (usually because of the logistical difficulties of construction), we can think of MOAT as defining the maximum area of the broad market environment within which the business has (by and large) freedom of action.

This is why, even though the individual business can do little to change these factors, understanding them is so important. Maximising opportunities means pressing forward in those areas in which the market environment is most welcoming. For example, you might find Government grants available to support SMEs in a particular business activity or new

regulations that require businesses to install safety equipment of the type that you manufacture. These are Opportunities - seize them with both hands.

In contrast, the market environment at its most hostile often poses threats - burdensome legislation, increased competition, dependency on a key customer whose own future is uncertain. You can't change them, but you can try to avoid these Threats.

In a later chapter, when we have completed a review of the growth implications of the **SPOTcheck®** Internal Factors and seen how the WEBS concept applies to these factors, we will combine both MOAT and WEBS visually as part of the business' strategy.

ANALYSING THE OPPORTUNITIES AND THE THREATS

Now is your chance, having worked through an analysis of the implications for the growth potential of your business of the five **SPOTcheck®** External Factors, to take an overview. Use the exercise below to help you.

OBJECTIVE
- To understand the MOAT principle
- To define strategic options from an external perspective

EXERCISE
ANALYSING OPPORTUNITIES AND THREATS

FACTOR	Opportunity/ Threat/ Neutral	How can you maximise the opportunity?	How can you avoid the threat?
1: Environment			
2: Market			
3: Customers			
4: Direct Competition			
5: Suppliers			

Now it's time to move onto the next **SPOTcheck®** Factor: **Promoters/ Management Team.**

OBJECTIVE

- To understand the impact of the promoters/ management team on the growth potential of the business
- To identify appropriate interventions to eliminate weaknesses and to build on strengths
- To define targets, actions and the resource implications of these
- To draft text for the business plan

SPOTcheck®
Score for this Factor

IMMEDIATE ACTIONS

Promoters/Management Team is the first of the **SPOTcheck®** Internal Factors - however, it is regarded as so critical to the successful growth of a business (thousands of research studies from all over the world confirm this) that it has been separated within **SPOTcheck®** from the other Internal factors.

As an Internal factor, it is the first to which the WEBS concept applies. You will see this building up through the links between the following chapters. In a later chapter, we will apply the WEBS concept visually and integrate it with the earlier MOAT concept to help you to represent your business' strategy.

As noted earlier, where we refer variously to the "promoters", the "management team" or the "promoters/ management team", in every case we mean the owner/manager, any equity shareholder actively involved in the business (spouses with nominal shareholdings for legal reasons are "family" not "management team") and key senior staff, whether or not they have an equity interest in the business, whose continued involvement is critical to the business.

ANALYSIS

It cannot be emphasised enough that the promoters and management team are the most critical determinant of a company's growth. Without able, committed management to drive the business forward, growth will not happen. Hence the importance of further analysis in this area.

SKILL LEVELS

Every stage of a company's life cycle demands different skills of management. The table on the next page shows the business life cycle, the issues that each stage brings, the key success factors for each stage and their relative importance.

FIGURE
BUSINESS LIFE CYCLE

STAGE	Survival	Consolidation	Control	Expansion
ISSUES	Owner **is** the business	Developing systems	Taking on and managing staff	Delegation and decentralization Market expansion
KEY PROBLEMS	Finding customers Managing cash-flow	Generating repeat sales Maintaining financial control	Fighting competition Developing new markets Control of margins/costs	Maintaining financial control
KEY SUCCESS FACTORS				
Owner				
Goals (personal & business)	3	1	3	3
Operational ability	3	3	2	2
Managerial ability	1	2	2	3
Strategic ability	1	2	3	3
Business				
Financial resources (cash/borrowing power)	3	3	2	3
Personnel resources (quality of staff, especially management)	1	1	3	2
System resources (information, planning and control systems)	1	2	3	3
Business resources (goodwill, market-share, technology, reputation, etc)	3	3	2	2

Drive, value and passion are internally driven and are hard to change. But skill levels can always be developed, whether "hard" skills (functional capabilities, such as marketing or financial skills), or "soft" skills, like dealing with people or managing change. You need to analyse the current skill levels of your management team and identify the new skills that the business will require in the future.

EXERCISE
SKILL LEVELS

	Current skills	Planned requirement	Skill Gap
What are your strong points?			
What are your weak points?			
What areas do you need to improve on?			
> Sales			
> Finance			
> Innovation/product development			
> Production			
> Marketing			
> Management			
> Communication			
> Negotiation			
> Change Management			
> Other (specify)			

BALANCE WITHIN THE MANAGEMENT TEAM

It's not enough to have the right skills (see the previous **Exercise**), you need them in the right balance. An organisation full of creative people still needs a boring fuddy-duddy who insists that the accounting system is kept up-to-date and that contracts are signed by customers for all major changes to specifications. The balance of skills among your management team must reflect the business that you are running - or plan to run, if major change is planned. Use this exercise to help you get the balance right.

EXERCISE
SKILL BALANCE

Take the answers from the previous **Exercise** for each of the management team and record them below. Identify imbalances and think about how you might correct them.

	Members of Management Team					Action Required
Skills	1	2	3	4	5	to correct imbalance
> Sales						
> Finance						
> Innovation/product development						
> Production						
> Marketing						
> Management						
> Communication						
> Negotiation						
> Change Management						
> Other (specify)						

EXERCISE
FILLING SKILL GAPS

	Source	Cost
How will you improve your skill levels?		
> Training		
> Advisers/consultants		
> Information system		
> Other (specify)		

EXERCISE
EXTERNAL EXPERTISE

	Used Now	Could be used in future
Sources of external expertise:		
> Accountant/Auditor		
> Solicitor		
> Consultant (specify topic)		
> Mentor		
> Other (specify)		

IMPROVING YOUR MANAGEMENT TEAM

Identifying skill deficits and imbalances in your management team may be an eye-opener, but it's only the first part of the task. It is important that you go on now to fill the gaps. Use the **Filling Skills Gaps** exercise to help.

You can also improve the skill levels of your business by buying-in external expertise. What sources of external expertise do you currently use? What more could you take advantage of?

Management is a common thread throughout the rest of this workbook. Within the remaining chapters relating to the **SPOTcheck®** Internal Factors, we will return again and again to the quality of the management team in the specific functional areas.

NETWORK/GOODWILL

Identifying and using external sources of expertise to assist you in growing your business leads naturally to using your network of contacts and benefiting from the goodwill within that network.

In an earlier Exercise in **Section 1** (page **6**), you (and each of your management team) identified your own personal network of friends, acquaintances and business contacts and considered how they might help you develop your business.

You should now repeat that exercise as a management team together. Remember that you are now including contacts that the business has in its own right - suppliers, customers, etc, in addition to the personal contacts of each member of the management team. What's interesting here is the extent of the overlaps - the networking - some of which you might not have been aware of before now.

**EXERCISE
BUSINESS NETWORKING**

Develop a profile of the business' current network along the following lines.

Contact organisation	Contact individual	Level of contact	Quality of contact	Nature of contact

How can these contacts be used to support the business' planned future growth?
Are they in a database?
If not, when will you put them into a database?

NON-EXECUTIVE DIRECTORS

A key resource for a growing business is a strong board of directors. In earlier exercises, you have already examined the skills and balance within your management team and looked at how external sources of expertise could assist with the development of the business. Would it help to bring some of the missing skills on board through the board of directors?

Non-executive directors with specific expertise in key functional areas or with cross-functional management skills, and especially those with experience of growth situations, can be of invaluable assistance to a growing business. In particular, non-executive directors usually bring an extensive network of contacts, built up through their experience in the industry. They may also bring partner technology, or credibility, or access to funding. Before you recruit a non-exec, you need to decide what you are looking for them to contribute.

The first question to ask is what do you want in a non-executive director. Use the exercise below to help you to decide this.

Managers are the basic, and scarcest, resource of any business enterprise.
PETER F DRUCKER

EXERCISE
NON-EXECUTIVE DIRECTORS

Do you want a non-executive director (tick all that apply):

As a sounding-board for ideas? ☐

As a source of advice based on previous experience? ☐

For hands-on assistance, perhaps in implementing something new in your business? ☐

For their contacts, to open doors that might otherwise be closed? ☐

For their expertise/experience in specific areas: Marketing, sales, finance, production, legal? ☐

For their market knowledge? ☐

The scarce resource today is management, knowledge, vision, dealing with change, recognising what people want and need in the future, and the ability to work together. You want find these scarce resources listed on a balance sheet.

MICHAEL MILKEN

Bringing a non-executive director onto your board will mean changes - mostly for the better, since the presence of an "outsider" will lend a certain formality to board meetings that may have been previously lacking.

The steps involved in appointing a non-executive director include:

- Involve all board members in the decision
- Ensure balance between existing and new members
- Define the specific background, experience, skills and personal qualities needed before beginning the selection process
- Identify potential candidates
- Describe and agree the conditions of appointment (length of the appointment, termination arrangements, etc)
- List core duties and periodic responsibilities (membership of specific board committees, minimum time to be spent on company/board matters, etc)
- Agree fees and expenses (amount, basis and frequency of payment)
- Agree confidentiality (non-disclosure, including any period after termination of the appointment, non-competition, etc)
- Other regulations (statutory and voluntary codes of practice).

How do you find a suitable non-executive director? Your earlier exercise on **Networks** may pinpoint a suitable individual. If not, Equity Network or the Institute of Directors (Ireland) Boardroom Centre or a number of other agencies may be able to help. In some cases, a mentor provided by an enterprise support agency may agree to join the company as a non-executive director.

CORPORATE GOVERNANCE AND THE ROLE OF THE BOARD

Enron and other business scandals of 2002 may seem light years away from the average SME, yet their fall-out will be - already is - a general tightening of regulation on the management of businesses of all sizes and a greater public emphasis on accountability in business.

Corporate governance is a grandious term for how your business is managed at the top: Who sits on your board of directors? Why? What do they contribute? What are their responsibilities? Who ensures that they discharge their obligations as directors? The implications of non-compliance are becoming more and more serious. As a director, you should check how the regulatory framework applies to your business.

EXERCISE
CORPORATE GOVERNANCE REGULATORY FRAMEWORK

	Statutory	Voluntary
What corporate governance regulation applies to your business, in relation to:		
> Responsibilities and Duties?		
> Powers?		
> Relationships with stakeholders?		
> Decision-making?		
> Administration?		
> Statutory provisions?		

The Board has four key responsibilities:
- Determining strategy and policy
- Monitoring progress
- Appointing senior management
- Accounting for the company's performance to stakeholders.

None of these responsibilities can be delegated.

The difference between directors and managers is that the ultimate responsibility, particularly in relation to legal and tax matters, rests with the Board. That's where the buck stops.

The Board should ensure clear communication between itself and the managers to whom it delegates operational responsibility. Although, in most smaller businesses, the same person may be both a director and a functional manager, it is important to ensure a clear separation between the two roles in your procedures and protocols.

CHANGE MANAGEMENT AND COMMUNICATION

Often overlooked in making the kind of significant changes that directed growth requires is the need to manage change and to communicate appropriately to all affected by it. You and your management team will be so caught up the excitement of what you are trying to achieve that you may forget about the other staff who, not knowing the full picture, see only the potential threats - to their jobs, to their status, to their overtime and bonuses, etc. Or customers may take offence at the fact that you no longer have time to return their phone calls and take their business elsewhere - even though the person to whom you have delegated this task is quite capable of dealing with all the customer's needs. Losing customers is not how you grow a business!

It's inevitable in change that someone will suffer. The famous philosopher, Anon, said: "*All change is bad - especially change for the better*". If you are serious about going forward, you must make sure that you bring your entire "team" - staff, customers, suppliers, all the "stakeholders" in your business - with you. Stragglers weaken the organisation.

Managing change means being honest and open about what you are trying to achieve and how you intend to achieve it. This is where rigorous planning of the sort that you are now undertaking will pay off. You will be surprised at just how detailed and penetrating some of the questions from the shop-floor will be - and more surprised at the negative effect of your inability to answer them. The key is regular, frequent and open communication - two-way communication, not lectures.

Change management needs leadership - and leadership starts with the leader(s). Check what kind of example you (and your fellow directors) set for your staff.

EXERCISE
LEADING BY EXAMPLE

Do you have a vision for the business?	☐ Yes ☐ No
Do you communicate it - at every opportunity?	☐ Yes ☐ No
Do you display confidence in yourself?	☐ Yes ☐ No
Do you display confidence in your	☐ Yes ☐ No
Do you communicate and expect high standards of performance?	☐ Yes ☐ No
Do you personally live and act the vision, values and standards that you have set for your business?	☐ Yes ☐ No
Do you demonstrate personal sacrifice, determination, persistence and courage?	☐ Yes ☐ No

Do you lead by example:
> Who is in the office the earliest in the morning?
> Who leaves the latest from the office?
> Who puts on the overalls when things get dirty?
> Who offers to make coffee when guest arrive?
> Who makes people laugh?
> Who makes the generous gestures to staff, suppliers and customers?

EXERCISE
WHAT ARE YOU WORTH?

The "normal" working year is based on a five-day week, 52 weeks a year, less 20 days holidays, less public holidays and some allowance for sick leave - say 230 working days, with 7.5 hours a day, giving a total of 1,725 hours a year (adjust this calculation for your own circumstances, if necessary).

How much do you how earn annually?

What is your hourly pay, based 1,725 hours a year?

How many hours do you really work (evenings, weekends and bank holidays)?

What is your hourly pay, based on your "real" time input?

What is the difference - in % terms?

Is this reduced rate a fair reflection of your value to the business? ☐ Yes ☐ No

Could someone else in the business who is earning less than your reduced hourly rate do some of the work that contributes to your extra time input?

(see the next exercise on **Delegation**)

EXERCISE
DELEGATION

Do you really want to take work home in the evenings/weekends? ☐ Yes ☐ No

What areas do you think you must deal with yourself?

What areas are most critical to the business?

What areas are you comfortable delegating to another person?

Delegate what to whom?

Develop a profile of the right person for each task you want to delegate and match your staff to the profiles.

DELEGATION

Finally, the owner/manager's worst nightmare - delegation!

Delegation is a critical management skill. There is plenty of guidance available in management texts on how to delegate and the advantages of doing so. The problem for most managers is not that they don't know how to delegate, it's that they don't want to - for owner/managers the "not wanting to" is even stronger, since they have a direct personal involvement in the business often from start-up. They see it as "letting go" - in effect, "letting down".

Each member of the management team should discuss these exercises with the others, to gain insights into where others consider they should/could/must delegate - and to whom - insights often denied to the individual themselves.

OUTPUT

Now that you have analysed the impact of the **SPOTcheck®** Internal Factor: Promoters / Management Team on the growth potential of your business, collate the results of your analysis. You will find this useful in **Section 4: Business Planning**.

OUTPUT	Planning(now)	ThisYear	NextYear	YearAfter
TARGETS				
ACTIONS				
RESOURCE IMPLICATIONS				
Time				
Money				
People				
Other				

OUTPUT TO BUSINESS PLAN	
Text	Information on promoters / management team; Corporate governance
Evidence	CVs of promoters / management team
Numbers	Resource implications - as above; Credit terms agreed with suppliers

NOTES

OBJECTIVE

- To understand the impact of strategy on the growth potential of the business
- To identify appropriate interventions to eliminate weaknesses and to build on strengths
- To define the strategic parameters ("strategic box") and guiding principles of the business
- To define targets, actions and the resource implications of these
- To draft text for the business plan

SPOTcheck®
Score for this Factor

IMMEDIATE ACTIONS

You have already had an opportunity to begin developing a strategy for your business (in **Section 1**). Go back and refresh your memory on the statements you wrote for your business:

- The values statement
- The passion statement
- The vision statement
- The mission statement.

Based on what you have learnt in analysing the implications of the **SPOTcheck®** External Factors and of the Promoters / Management Team on the growth potential of your business, you may want to revisit these statements. Certainly, as you work through the later chapters of this workbook, it is likely that you will revisit these statements several times. That's a normal part of the process of business planning.

Next, look back at the target(s) that you set for your business in **Section 1**. Again, based on your knowledge to date, you may want to revise these. Certainly, as you work through the later sections of this workbook, it is likely that you will revise these targets several times. Again, that's a normal part of the process of business planning.

ANALYSIS

In the current business environment, it is very difficult to plan ahead because so much changes so fast. Some people argue therefore that there is no point in planning. But this argument overlooks the distinction between strategy and implementation within the planning process. It may be difficult to accurately forecast the route you will take to reach your destination, but unless you know where you are headed, how will you know that you are on the right road? It is because of the difficulty in planning ahead that planning is so important.

Your values, passion, vision and mission statements (see **Section 1**) are key determinants in plotting your direction. The next statements that you need to think about - and write - in order to complete your strategy are:

- The positioning statement
- The resourcing statement.

Frankly, you will have difficulty in writing the positioning statement until you have worked through the chapter on **Marketing** that follows - and writing the resourcing statement will be equally difficult until you have virtually completed the process of business planning (this whole section of the workbook).

However, we introduce these two statements now so that you can see how they contribute to the overall development of a strategy for a growing business. After all, you may not be able to hang pictures on the wall of a new house until it has been fully built, painted and furnished but there's nothing stopping you from buying a painting at any time. In the same way, although you cannot complete your strategy until all the pieces are in place, you can begin to see the shape of the overall jigsaw and of the missing pieces at an early stage.

A POSITIONING STATEMENT FOR YOUR BUSINESS

A positioning statement sets out how you want your business to be perceived by the market - your customers and your direct competitors.

It is different from your vision statement, which sets out how you perceive your business.

VISION is where you want to be.

POSITIONING is where the market thinks you are.

You will look in more detail at positioning statements in the chapter on **Marketing**. For now, try this exercise to get you thinking.

EXERCISE
SEVEN KEY WORDS

Write down seven words that describe your business - for example: Exciting, bright, young, cool, energetic, expensive and vibrant.

A RESOURCING STATEMENT FOR YOUR BUSINESS

A resourcing statement sets out three things:

- What your current resources (cash, assets, people, intangibles, etc) are.
- What constraints you currently face (lack of investment, pressure on directors' time, etc).
- What resources you need to implement your growth strategy.

You probably have some sense of this statement now but you really need to work through the rest of this workbook and come back to it later (see the chapter on **Use of Financial Resources**).

STRATEGIC BOX

The **"strategic box"** is a visual representation of your strategy, formed by:

- Your six statements - values, passion, vision, mission, positioning and resourcing
- Your targets.

From these, your tactics - the specific actions you must undertake in order to achieve your strategy - and your direction will become clear.

The strategic box is represented visually below.

Competitive strategy involves positioning a business to maximise the value of the capabilities that distinguish it from its competitors.

MICHAEL PORTER

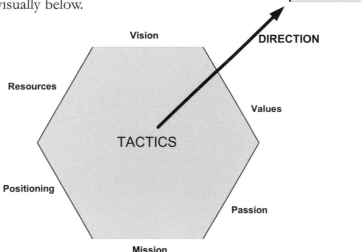

Each of the six statements forms a side of a hexagon. It is within this hexagon that the business operates. All tactical and operating decisions are determined by the six statements - the sides of the hexagon.

Using the sailing analogy from **Section 1**, the strategic box is a boat at sea. A glass panel has been let into the bottom of the boat, through which you can see the underlying environment clearly - everything else is obscured. The size and shape of the glass panel determines how much you can see. Floating, the boat is at the mercy of the sea (the environment) unless you give it direction by steering it and propelling it. Your strategy (your boat) will simply drift with market trends (the tide/current), unless you turn on the engine and steer to where you want to go. And your only sens eof direction is given by the glass panel (your strategic box).

The importance of the six statements that make up your strategy is that they give you a larger - or smaller - window onto the environment within which your business operates. The more you can see, the better you can decide the short-term tactical changes that are necessary to avoid threats or maximise opportunities, while still holding direction for your longer-term targets.

GUIDING PRINCIPLES

Once the parameters for your business' strategic box are agreed, the next step is formulate guiding principles to help you communicate with staff.

Targets are one way to communicate your strategy. But very often, targets are too big for staff to be able to see day-to-day how they direct operational activities. Staff may understand that your aim is to sail around the world but they may still have difficulty deciding what to do entering or leaving harbour.

So you need a set of guiding principles that brings the targets and strategy down-to-earth.

Strategy tells your staff **"what"** - the guiding principles tell them **"how"**.

Because your company is operating in a volatile and often hostile environment, in which it is difficult to be prescriptive in advance, it is useful to have a set of guiding principles to which your staff - and you yourself - can refer as the need arises.

For example, your guiding principles might be something like these:

- We will give the customer the best advice possible always, even when this means that we have to direct them to a competitor's product instead of selling them our own less suitable product.
- We will be honest in our dealings with customers and suppliers always .
- We will travel always by the most economical means possible - "first class" has no place in this company, except in relation to customer service.
- We will pay for all reasonable training costs incurred by staff in their own personal development.
- We will seek always to promote from within the company, before looking for outside candidates.

How many guiding principles do you need? You must decide for yourself. Most businesses need at least three or four; few can cope with more than 10. Six or eight is a good starting point. Be prepared to add and revise principles as necessary.

EXERCISE
GUIDING PRINCIPLES

Write down some principles to guide you, your staff and your business.

1.

2.

3.

4.

5.

6.

7.

8.

9.

10.

COMMUNICATING YOUR STRATEGY

The guiding principles you have just developed will not work unless you keep a range of parties - most especially your own staff - informed. That means an emphasis on communication - mainly internal but some external. Communication is a weak spot of most businesses and, when they are growing, there never seems to be enough time.

However, when you have written the six statements that make up your strategy, you have a communication tool to explain the philosophy of your business in relation to, among other things:

- The environment
- The way in which you do business and what you plan to achieve
- Staff, customers and suppliers
- The community within which your business is based.

The statements can be used both internally (your staff and suppliers) and externally (your customers and the community you are working within). Trends show that customers are starting to take Value and Mission statements seriously and expect businesses to develop a social conscience. Make sure that your statements are in line with what your customers expect.

Your company's statements must be shared and explained to all your staff. They are not secrets. They set out the way in which you do business for all to see. If your staff don't know what how to do business in the way that you want, how can they work for you?

FINALISING YOUR TARGETS

At this stage, you have defined the parameters of your strategic box, and you have written and communicated your guiding principles - the next step is to finalise your targets. Go back to **Section 1** and review your targets. Re-define them, if necessary.

REVIEWING YOUR STRATEGY

Before your task is complete, you should review your strategy as a whole. You may need to do this several times, as you continuously refine it.

EXERCISE
STRATEGY REVIEW

To review your strategy, consider :
Focus - On what?
Growth, decline, stabilisation - How is your market developing?
Maintain existing markets - Will this be enough?
Life cycle of the product - What stage are you at?
New markets - Where? At what cost?
New products - How?
National or international - What are your ambitions?
Broad market or niche market - Where are you aiming?
Innovation - What part will it play?
Small steps or big steps - Which are you most comfortable with?

OUTPUT

Now that you have analysed the impact of the **SPOTcheck®** Internal Factor: Strategy on the growth potential of your business, collate the results of your analysis. You will find this useful in **Section 4: Business Planning**.

Strategy has to be subversive.
If it is not challenging company rules or industry rules, it's not strategy.

GARY HAMEL

NOTE: All exercises and forms are available for download and completion at **www.growingabusinessinireland.com**.

OUTPUT	Planning(now)	ThisYear	NextYear	YearAfter
TARGETS				
ACTIONS				
RESOURCE IMPLICATIONS				
Time				
Money				
People				
Other				

OUTPUT TO BUSINESS PLAN	
Text	Positioning statement; Resourcing statement; "Strategic box"; Guiding principles; Targets
Evidence	
Numbers	Resource implications - as above; Credit terms agreed with suppliers

NOTES

SPOTcheck®
Score for this Factor

IMMEDIATE ACTIONS

ANALYSIS

You have identified your markets, your customers and your direct competitors.

You have a vision for your business.

From all this, you can now develop a positioning statement (see chapter on **Strategy**), which will determine your branding and marketing strategy.

POSITIONING STATEMENT

A positioning statement sets out how you want your business to be perceived by the market - your customers and your direct competitors.

It is different from your vision statement, which sets out how you perceive your business.

Vision is where you want to be.

Positioning is where the market thinks you are.

So, for example, your vision statement might be:

To own and operate a chain of 20 profitable computer re-selling stores in more than 10 key cities by 2015.

Your positioning statement for the same business might read:

We will position XYZ Computers Stores as a friendly, accessible, knowledgeable, well-designed and up-to-the-minute place to buy the widest range of computers and software at the lowest prices and with the longest opening hours in each town where we have a store.

You may find it helpful in writing a positioning statement to substitute the words "Customers will see ..." in place of "we will position ...". For example, the positioning statement above could be re-drafted to read:

Customers will see XYZ Computers Stores as a friendly, accessible, knowledgeable, well-designed and up-to-the-minute place to buy the widest range of computers and software at the lowest prices and with the longest opening hours in each town where we have a store.

This positioning statement determines:
- The type and quality of staff - friendly and knowledgeable, willing to work extended opening hours
- The design of the stores - well-designed
- The location of the stores - accessible
- Pricing - lowest prices
- Purchasing - consistent with lowest prices

- The number of staff - to cover extended opening hours
- Competitiveness - willingness to stay open and price lower than other computer retailers locally.

Immediately, you can see the power of the positioning statement - and this is only scratching the surface. Since it is written from the point of view of your customers, giving their perception of your business, it's critical for your marketing.

Now write a positioning statement for your business. Remind yourself, if necessary of your vision statement.

**EXERCISE
POSITIONING STATEMENT**

Write a positioning statement for your business.

---

*There are not a lot of client-related problems.
There is only one:
Some of us don't take good enough care of our clients.*

THOMAS J WATSON, founder, IBM

It's easy to write a positioning statement. But, if your desired position is far removed from your current position as perceived by your customers, then you have a massive investment ahead of you. The wider the gap, the more resources you will need to invest to bridge the gap. For example, imagine the investment in marketing and customer service that Ryanair would have to make in order to establish itself in business travellers' minds as a premium service airline. Its current successful positioning - as a "low fares" airline - is too far removed from the premium position to be achieved except at great cost.

To check whether your positioning statement is a true reflection of the market perception, compare it to your customers' perceptions that you identified earlier in the chapter on **Customers.**

BRANDING

In effect, your positioning is your branding.

But branding is only of value if you can achieve the position you have set out for your business in the positioning statement.

Branding may also apply to individual products or services - you may need to write a positioning statement for each. This is how large companies cater for the entire breadth of the market-place - not with a single brand but with a series of brands, each positioned to capture a different market segment. Think of the French hotel chain, Accor, whose brands range from Formule 1 motels, through Ibis, Mercure and Novotel, often with several hotels under the different brand names in major cities.

You achieve your branding/positioning through your marketing strategy.

One of the things you are trying to do is to gain "mind-share" or "heart-share", which leads to market-share.

"Mind-share" is the immediate calling to mind of your brand in customers' minds when they need the type of product or service you provide. For example, for most people, Amazon.com is synonymous with buying books on the Web.

"Heart-share" is the positive feeling that customers have towards your brand, which leads them to seek to it out even when other alternatives are available. How many times have you driven past several petrol stations in order to get to your favourite petrol station?

MARKETING STRATEGY

Your marketing strategy for the business begins to fill in the gaps in your overall strategy. What you are communicating through your marketing strategy is the marketing mix you have chosen. This will be different for each product, service and revenue stream - but there's usually a significant level of overlap (it's hard to market one product as a "quality" item when you market others as "low-cost substitutes for well-known brands").

As an example of the marketing mix at work, take perfume. Broken down to its essentials, perfume is nothing more than water with a smell. But the price that customers pay for perfume is many times the value of water. Why?

Because the marketing mix has been so well-crafted that the customers' image of perfume is that of an exclusive, special, luxurious, sensual product - far removed from our crude description of it as "water with a smell". The image in customers' minds is created with the building blocks of the marketing mix: Price, product, place and promotion. Let's see how:

- **Product:** The product is essentially water with a smell. However, customers see something more than this, because perfume is sold in a sophisticated and well-designed bottle, with expensive-looking packaging. Because it looks expensive, customers begin to think that it is expensive

- **Price:** The cost price (excluding packaging) of perfume is perhaps less than €/£1 per bottle. If it is sold for many times that, the customers' perception again changes. If it is expensive, it must be special

- **Place:** Perfume is not sold at every local shop but is only available from expensive-looking retail shops that already have an up-market image. This makes the product exclusive (or

appear so). And again, the customers' perception of the product changes - if the product appears exclusive, it must be so.

- **Promotion:** Perfume is not sold by local leaflet drops or mass mailings, but is promoted by elegant life-style advertisements on national television and in glossy up-market magazines. Again, this changes customers' perception of the product, driving it further up-market and justifying in the customer's mind the high retail price.

By using the right combinations of the different elements in the marketing mix, you can determine how customers perceive your product/service. Place, promotion and product are covered in the next two chapters; here we look at price.

PRICE

As part of your growth strategy, you should re-examine your pricing policy for each of your products/services/revenue streams. You have already examined your pricing in the context of your direct competition, in the chapter on **Direct Competition** earlier .

EXERCISE
PRICING

Work through this exercise for each product/service/revenue stream:

	Current	Planned
How is your price made up?		
o Materials		
o Time		
o Machine cost		
o Other		
o Total costs		
o Profit margin		
o Selling price		

What are customers accustomed to paying already?
What are your competitors' prices (on average)?
What is your price?
What do you want your price to say about your product/service?

CHANNEL PRICING

Your choice of distribution system has a direct effect on your profit margin, since every element in the channel will get a portion of the final price.

You must decide whether the added value of a particular distribution system outweighs the costs involved. For example, a distribution system might offer you access to existing and new customer groups, access to an established image, assistance in selling products, cheaper promotion, etc. - but at a cost of a reduced margin. Direct marketing through mail order, direct sales and the Internet will save you the discounts payable in traditional channels but require a higher investment in marketing and promotion.

Note: Discounts on the retail price given within channels of distribution - "trade" or "channel" pricing - are not the same as price reductions given to customers (special offers). Use the exercise to help you decide your channel pricing policy.

PRICE EROSION

The concept of price "erosion" is used to illustrate how the price the customer pays gets whittled down through the various channels until the originators of the product or service receive their share. Analyse your current price erosion.

CREDIT TERMS

The importance of credit terms lies in their impact on cash-flow. If you have access to financial modelling software, use it to explore the cash-flow effect of different credit terms.

EXERCISE
CHANNEL PRICING POLICY

	Current	Planned
What type of channel discounts do different channels receive?		
What is the added value of the different distribution approaches?		
What channel prices do you offer?		
What flexibility do you offer in this channel pricing policy?		

EXERCISE
PRICE EROSION

	%	€/£
Retail price	100	
Less VAT/Sales tax		
Less Retailer's share		
Less Wholesaler's share		
Your selling price		

EXERCISE
CREDIT TERMS

	Current	Planned
Do you offer credit?	☐ Yes ☐ No	☐ Yes ☐ No
If "Yes", to whom and on what basis?		
If "No", why not? Is this standard in your industry?		
Summarise the impact of your credit terms in the table:		

What percentage of your sales is/will be paid:	Current %	Planned %
Within 0 to 30 days?		
Within 31 to 60 days?		
Within 61 to 90 days?		
Within 91 to 120 days?		
In more than 120 days?		

Of most interest in this exercise are the changes between your current credit terms and those you plan offer. If you plan to reduce credit terms, what effect will it have on your cash-flow - and on your sales?

You might also develop further insight into your policy by considering the following:

- If you do give credit, what level of non-payment (bad debts) do you suffer? How could this be reduced? With what impact on sales?
- If you don't give credit, what damage does this policy cause to your sales?

MARKETING MANAGEMENT

The quality of the marketing management can be seen in two gaps:

- Between the current level of skills identified (see the chapter on **Promoters / Management Team**) and those needed for the future
- Between the current positioning of the company and its positioning statement.

How will you fill the gap(s)? The choices are set out in the exercise below.

EXERCISE
MARKETING MANAGEMENT - FILLING THE GAP

The gap identified between current and future needs in marketing management is best filled by:

> Training the existing management team	☐
> Support from a mentor	☐
> Advice and guidance from a consultant	☐
> Recruiting a non-executive director	☐
> Recruiting an executive director	☐

OUTPUT

Now that you have analysed the impact of the **SPOTcheck®** Internal Factor: Marketing on the growth potential of your business, collate the results of your analysis. You will find this useful in **Section 4: Business Planning**.

OUTPUT	Planning(now)	ThisYear	NextYear	YearAfter
TARGETS				
ACTIONS				
RESOURCE IMPLICATIONS				
Time				
Money				
People				
Other				
OUTPUT TO BUSINESS PLAN				
Text	Positioning statement; Resourcing statement; "Strategic box"; Guiding principles; Targets			
Evidence				
Numbers	Resource implications - as above; Credit terms agreed with suppliers			

OBJECTIVE

OBJECTIVE

- To understand the impact of sales/ promotion/ channels on the growth potential of the business
- To identify appropriate interventions to eliminate weaknesses and to build on strengths
- To define sales forecast
- To define targets, actions and the resource implications of these
- To draft text for the business plan

SPOTcheck®
Score for this Factor

IMMEDIATE ACTIONS

CHANNELS

Because you are already in business, you understand the channels of distribution that you use for your product. Each industry is different and fortunes have been made (and lost) on changes to the channels of distribution. Look at how Dell and Gateway have changed the way people buy computers.

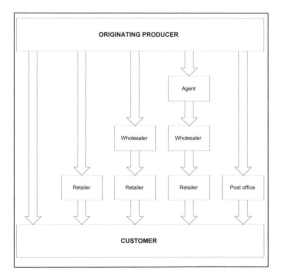

The diagram above summarises the main channels and the stages within them. The fewer stages, the lower the distribution cost - which is why lots of businesses try to cut out the middleman. On the other hand, the middleman provides a useful service - holding stock, sourcing customers, advising on market conditions - and cannot always be dispensed with. You need to balance distribution costs with promotion costs. Very often, sales channels with low distribution costs have high promotion costs.

Channels are your routes to market. As channels become increasingly concentrated under the control of a smaller number of organizations, they are increasingly difficult to access - and thus increasingly critical to growth. If you can't find a route to market, how will your customer be able to buy your product?

Second, alternatives such as the Internet have not only begun to replace existing channels in many industries - obliterating existing channels in some, like in airline ticket-buying - but they have changed customer's expectations. If you can buy your seat on a Ryanair flight on the Internet in a few minutes, why can't you do that for a theatre seat, or a restaurant booking , or for lots of other things?

You already know your channels. Check how well you know them in the next exercise.

EXERCISE
CHANNELS OF DISTRIBUTION

Which channels do you use/plan to use (tick all that apply)?

	Current	Planned
Retail	☐	☐
Wholesale	☐	☐
Catalogue	☐	☐
Agents	☐	☐
Alliances/partners	☐	☐
Web	☐	☐
Networks	☐	☐

Is timing of delivery crucial or are clients prepared to wait for delivery?

> Timing crucial ☐

> Prepared to wait ☐

Does the product/service need explanation or installation?

> Explanation ☐

> Installation ☐

Is it to be available:

> Exclusively? ☐

> Selectively? ☐

> Anywhere possible? ☐

What outlets do you use for your product/service?

What outlets do customers associate with your product?

Does the image of the outlet(s) chosen reflect your image?	☐ Yes	☐ No
Does it complement your product or service?	☐ Yes	☐ No
Does it fit with your values?	☐ Yes	☐ No
Do you deliver dircctly to the customer?	☐ Yes	☐ No
Do you give people a choice in delivery?	☐ Yes	☐ No
Have you considered network marketing?	☐ Yes	☐ No

If "Yes", how will you organise network marketing for your product/service?

If "No", why not?

How does your main competitor organise its distribution?

I am the world's worst salesman, therefore I must make it easy for people to buy.

FW WOOLWORTH

Use this exercise to spark your thinking about alternative channels. Creative use of new channels of distribution - new routes to market - can add value for the customer, increase your profit margins and help your positioning. Find some today!

If your channels include exports, work through the exercise on the next page.

NOTE: All exercises and forms are available for download and completion at **www.growingabusinessinireland.com**.

EXERCISE
EXPORT CHECKLIST

1. How specific are your plans? Are they an integral part of your business plan and strategy for the business?
2. Which products or services do you want to export?
3. Which countries do you want to export to and in which order of priority?
4. What is your target market/segments within the market?
5. Have you done desk research on your export markets?
6. Have you actually visited the countries involved?
7. Do you have sales experience in your proposed export markets?
8. Do you have the language skills needed?
9. Have you organised your administration for foreign payments and customs/excise regulations?
10. Are you familiar with the regulations relating to your products/services in your export markets?
11. Does your product or service need adjustment? For   safety, environment, quality, packaging, taste, fashion, culture or language?
12. Is your price, after calculation of the extra costs involved in exporting, still competitive?
13. What are your turnover targets: per country, per market, per segment?
14. Do you have enough time available to build and develop the export market?
15. Who will be responsible for marketing and sales abroad?
16. Is your organisation, from telephonist to after sales, ready and prepared for export and dealing internationally?
17. Can your business cope with the demands of foreign markets: Delivery times, transport, quantities?
18. Which channels are you planning to use in your export markets?
19. Do you have the right promotion and instruction materials?
20. Are your term and conditions, contracts, quotes, etc. translated and adjusted to your export markets?

PROMOTION

Promotion can achieve:
- **Awareness:** Make customers aware of your existence - advertising is good for this
- **Image:** Create the right perception in customers of your products/services - public relations is good at this
- **Information:** Communicate information (perhaps technical specifications) to your customers - advertising or trade shows are good at this
- **Sales:** Generate actual orders - direct mail is suited to this.

How do you use your current promotion spend? Use last year's figures in the exercise below.

EXERCISE
LAST YEAR'S PROMOTION SPEND

	Awareness €/£	Image €/£	Information €/£	Sales €/£	Total €/£	Sales Results €/£
Advertising						
Public relations						
Trade shows						
Direct mail						
Internet						
Personal selling						
Other						
Total						
% of Total Promotion Spend					100	

How should you use your promotion spend in future?

In addition to judging it on the basis of the results achieved last year, your positioning statement should inform your spending decisions.

EXERCISE
PROMOTION TARGETS

Based on the breakdown of your current promotion spend between awareness, image, information and sales-generating activities, how do you plan to use future promotional spending?

Set quantifiable targets for each of type of activity (for example, to increase sales volume by 10% or increase awareness by 40% in a specific sector of the market).

	Current focus%	Planned focus%	Target
Awareness			
Image			
Information			
Sales			

How will you measure achievement of these targets?
Who is the promotional activity targeted at?
What is the time frame for the promotional activity?

EXERCISE
NEXT YEAR'S PROMOTION SPEND

	Awareness €/£	Image €/£	Information €/£	Sales €/£	Total €/£	Sales Forecast €/£
Advertising						
Public relations						
Trade shows						
Direct mail						
Internet						
Personal selling						
Other						
Total						
% of Total Promotion Spend				100		

Your promotional spend should link in with your sales forecasts. Each aspect of your spend should contribute to achieving the sales that you have planned. Use the exercise on the next page to help you understand the link between promotional spend and sales.

Sales means selling the product you are marketing.

STEPHEN O'CONNOR, CEO, Glanbia

EXERCISE
SALES FORECASTS

	Products/product groups				Promotion budget		
	A	B	C	Total	Sales	Other	Total
UNIT SALES							
Jan							
Feb							
Mar							
Apr							
May							
Jun							
Jul							
Aug							
Sep							
Oct							
Nov							
Dec							
Total							
Price							
Total sales value							
Number of customers							
Average sale per customer - value							
Average sale per customer- units							

SALES MANAGEMENT

According to Enterprise Ireland, one of the key success factors in the growth of businesses is the ability to sell, to deliver on sales forecasts.

This means two things.

First, small companies need to be able to "punch above their weight" - to take on as equals businesses many times larger than themselves. Are you up to negotiating a licensing deal for your software with Microsoft?

Second, sales is not just about big deals - it's about keeping a flow of deals going, whether they are big, small and inbetween.

Since the size of the deals that your business does has an impact on its costs and its sales management structure, analyse last year's figures in the exercise below.

It's not only size that matters, the length of time it takes to bring a deal to fruition is also important. Some businesses work on very short sales cycle - a fruit and vegetable store has an almost instant sales cycle, since stock must be sold while it's still fresh. On the other hand, an aircraft manufacturer might pursue a customer for two years before securing an order (and then take two more years to deliver it!).

Re-analyse last year's sales figures in the exercise below, this time for the length of time they took to bring to fruition.

EXERCISE
LAST YEAR'S SALES BY SIZE OF DEAL

Size	Definition	Value €/£	%	Volume €/£	%
Small					
Medium					
Large					
Total			100		100

Experienced sales professionals talk about the "sales pipeline". They know that you must be always generating new leads, persuading potential customers to see demonstrations, if you are to keep the flow of sales coming through. Many sales people break down their sales prospects by stage in the pipeline and actively monitor the pipeline to ensure that prospects move through it to become customers.

There is a clear link between the last question in the exercise above and the promotion activities that your business engages in.

As a key function and driving force of the company, sales need to be managed carefully. Your work on strategy to date should have identified the main focus:

- Channel management
- Retail management
- E-commerce management
- Sales management
- Communication management.

Sales is all! Marketing, positioning, strategy are all essential but are only instruments to achieve sales. In the end, it's sales that drives the business.

The quality of the sales management can be seen in two gaps:

- Between the current level of skills identified (see the chapter on **Promoters / Management Team**) and those needed for the future
- Between the current positioning of the company and its positioning statement.

How will you fill the gap(s)? The choices are set out in the exercise below.

EXERCISE
LAST YEAR'S SALES BY LENGTH OF TIME TO ACHIEVE

Time from first contact to invoiced sale	Value €/£	Value %	Volume €/£	Volume %
Instant				
Within a week				
Within a month				
Within 3 months				
Within 6 months				
Within 12 months				
More than 12 months				
Total		100		100

EXERCISE
SALES PIPELINE

What are the stages in your current sales pipeline?
How full is your pipeline?
What big deals are on the way?
How many are close to completion?
How long on average does a deal take to go through the pipeline?
What do you need to do to generate more in your pipeline?

EXERCISE
SALES MANAGEMENT - FILLING THE GAP

The gap identified between current and future needs in sales management is best filled by:

> Training the existing management team ☐
> Support from a mentor ☐
> Advice and guidance from a consultant ☐
> Recruiting a non-executive director ☐
> Recruiting an executive director ☐

OUTPUT

Now that you have analysed the impact of the **SPOTcheck®** Internal Factor: **Sales / Promotion / Channels** on the growth potential of your business, collate the results of your analysis. You will find this useful in **Section 4: Business Planning**.

OUTPUT	Planning(now)	ThisYear	NextYear	YearAfter
TARGETS				
ACTIONS				
RESOURCE IMPLICATIONS				
Time				
Money				
People				
Other				

OUTPUT TO BUSINESS PLAN	
Text	Channel description; Promotion targets
Evidence	Channel analysis; Promotion analysis
Numbers	Resource implications - as above; Credit terms agreed with suppliers

NOTES

SPOTcheck®
Score for this Factor

IMMEDIATE ACTIONS

OBJECTIVE
- To understand the impact of products/services on the growth potential of the business
- To identify appropriate interventions to eliminate weaknesses and to build on strengths
- To define targets, actions and the resource implications of these
- To draft text for the business plan

ANALYSIS

The starting point here is your current products, services and revenue streams - and how they might change in the future.

Your product/service is key to your growth. But, because it is so familiar to you, there is a danger that you forget to view it from your customers' perspective. Use these exercises to help you re-orientate.

EXERCISE
PRODUCTS AND SERVICES

	Current	Planned

For each of your current products and services, describe briefly your product(s)/service(s):

CORE ELEMENTS:

Function: What does it do?

Packaging: How is it presented?

Design: Is it modern or old-fashioned?

Features: What features does it offer?

Price: How much?

Integrity: Does it do what it promises?

SERVICE ELEMENTS:

Before-sales service: Brochures, information on product use, etc

During-sales service: More information, costs comparisons, advice on use

After-sales service: Dealing with problems, breakdowns, etc

Guarantees: Promises to fix the product if anything goes wrong

Warranties: Fixing what's gone wrong, when it does

Delivery: May be important for bulky items

Availability: Customers hate waiting once they have decided to buy something

Add-ons: Extra features to improve performance, ease-of-use, etc

Finance: To help them afford the purchase.

INTANGIBLE ELEMENTS

Quality perceptions

Value perceptions

Reputation

Brand name

Corporate image

Other users' recommendations.

Twenty-four out of twenty-five products do not survive the test of the market-place.

DAVID OGILVY

EXERCISE
PRODUCTS AND SERVICES - CUSTOMER PERSPECTIVE

What are the main reasons that people buy your product or service?

Do they repeat-buy it?	☐ Yes	☐ No

If "Yes", why?

If "No", why not?

Are any improvements/changes to existing products/services planned?	☐ Yes	☐ No

If "Yes", why?

If "No", why not?

Are any new products/services planned?	☐ Yes	☐ No

If "Yes", why?

If "No", why not?

Are any new markets for existing products/services planned?	☐ Yes	☐ No

If "Yes", why?

If "No", why not?

Do your current product/services fit with:

> Your values?	☐ Yes	☐ No
> Your passion?	☐ Yes	☐ No
> Your vision?	☐ Yes	☐ No
> Your positioning?	☐ Yes	☐ No

EXERCISE
DIFFERENTIATION

How do you distinguish it from similar products?

How do you make it recognisable?

How do you make different versions of your product recognisable?

EXERCISE
QUALITY - IN THE EYE OF THE BEHOLDER

What does quality mean to you?

What does it mean for your customer?

What does it mean for your product/service?

DIFFERENTIATION

Differentiating your product or service from similar products or services from your competitors is key to maximising the price you can sell it for. The more unique your product appears to be, the more you can sell it for.

QUALITY

Quality is an attitude of mind that results in everyone in a business working together towards:

• Eliminating (or minimising) errors and faults
• Meeting deadlines
• Mapping out clear lines of responsibility
• Continuous improvement.

QUALITY SYSTEMS

Quality systems help ensure that quality is delivered every time.

Quality certification provides independent assurance that the quality systems you have implemented meet approved standards. Surveys show that quality assurance marks/logos give customers valued guidance when buying products and services and that they influence customers' decisions to buy at point of sale. However, few companies trading in Ireland have either the Q-Mark or ISO 9000 certification.

OUTPUT

Now that you have analysed the impact of the **SPOTcheck®** Internal Factor: **Product / Service** on the growth potential of your business, collate the results of your analysis. You will find this useful in **Section 4: Business Planning**.

EXERCISE
QUALITY STANDARDS

Which quality standards are relevant to your business?
Which of these do you hold?
Which are you working towards achieving?
Would achieving a quality standard (in addition to any you already hold) support your positioning?
Would achieving a quality standard (in addition to any you already hold) support your growth?

OUTPUT	Planning(now)	ThisYear	NextYear	YearAfter
TARGETS				
ACTIONS				
RESOURCE IMPLICATIONS				
Time				
Money				
People				
Other				

OUTPUT TO BUSINESS PLAN	
Text	Product analysis and descriptions
Evidence	Market research
Numbers	Resource implications - as above; Credit terms agreed with suppliers

11: PROCESS

OBJECTIVE

- To understand the impact of process on the growth potential of the business
- To identify appropriate interventions to eliminate weaknesses and to build on strengths
- To define the business model
- To define targets, actions and the resource implications of these
- To draft text for the business plan

ANALYSIS

Each organisation has its own specific process but, according to the National Institute for Transport and Logistics (NITL), there are core activities, some or all of which every business will require.

These are:

- Buy
- Make
- Move
- Sell.

In developing your growth plan, you must think through your process and the activities that are relevant to your situation. You will also need to identify the resources and people needed to establish and maintain those functions.

CURRENT PROCESS

Think about your product or service. What are the stages in its movement through the business, from the stage when a potential customer phones for a price to the delivery of the product or service? What activities are involved?

Map your process in the exercise.

OUT-SOURCING

Now look at your process using the NITL model and consider where out-sourcing could be used.

EXERCISE PROCESS

Look at your company.
Describe your operation:
> Size
> Layout of premises
> Furniture
> Phone systems
> People

How do things get done?
Is it busy or quiet?
Does it appear organised?
Who does what?
How are customers' orders fulfilled?
How are products made?
From what?
With what?
What machinery is used?
Where is inventory stored?
What items are used to make the products?
How are your products delivered to customers?
How are your services delivered?
What equipment do you need for your services?

COMPETITOR ANALYSIS

The next step is to look at your process or business model in the context of your competitors in the exercise on the next page.

E-COMMERCE

The dot-com/dot-bomb has made many business people weary/wary of e-commerce. Nonetheless, e-commerce is here to stay.

For growing businesses, it has two major potential applications:

• As a source of new markets - the Web brings within reach customers that previously could not be reached let alone sold to

• As a source of cost-savings in internal processes - electronic transmission of data can sometimes take significant costs out of the supply chain.

There are plenty of examples of business that have made significant - even, in some cases, spectacular - savings in their internal processes through the application of Internet/e-commerce technology. Check with your industry associations for examples, look on the Web itself or read about them in the technical press.

REDEFINING YOUR PROCESS

Caught up in the day-today, it's difficult ot look objectively at the process you use. The exercises you have just completed will help you look at everyday routines with new eyes. But use the next exercise to take it one step further and to redefine your process, in the context of the investment it will require.

EXERCISE
OUT-SOURCING

Of the four core activities, which could your business outsource?

	Completely	Partly
Buy	☐	☐
Make	☐	☐
Move	☐	☐
Sell	☐	☐

Where do your business' "core competencies" lie?
What is the business really good at? (review your business' Passion statement)
Where can the business gain competitive advantage?

EXERCISE
COMPETITORS' PROCESSES

How do your competitors organise their process/business model?
What is your most progressive competitor doing?
What is happening in other countries in your industry?

EXERCISE
E-COMMERCE

How could e-commerce affect your process in the following areas?
> Buy
> Make
> Move
> Sell

How should you react to these changes?
> Invest ahead of trends and use technology as a competitive weapon
> Follow what my competitors do
> Wait and see
> Put my "head in the sand"

EXERCISE
REDEFINE YOUR PROCESS

Describe your process as altered by the review above.
Do the changes you plan require new investment?
How much? Why?
Where arc the benefits of the investment felt:
> In the process itself?
> From the customer's perspective?
What value is added for customers?
To what extent, as a result of the investment, can you:
> Improve your margins?
> Increase prices?
> Deter competitors?
> Increase market share?

EXERCISE
PROCESS MANAGEMENT - FILLING THE GAP

The gap identified between current and future needs in process management is best filled by:

> Training the existing management team ☐
> Support from a mentor ☐
> Advice and guidance from a consultant ☐
> Recruiting a non-executive director ☐
> Recruiting an executive director ☐

There's a better to do it.
Find it!

THOMAS A EDISON

PROCESS MANAGEMENT

The quality of the process management can be seen in two gaps:

• Between the current level of skills identified (see the chapter on **Promoters / Management Team**) and those needed for the future
• Between the current positioning of the company and its positioning statement.

How will you fill the gap(s)? The choices are set out in the exercise.

OUTPUT

Now that you have analysed the impact of the **SPOTcheck®** Internal Factor: **Process** on the growth potential of your business, collate the results of your analysis. You will find this useful in **Section 4: Business Planning**.

OUTPUT	Planning(now)	ThisYear	NextYear	YearAfter
TARGETS				
ACTIONS				
RESOURCE IMPLICATIONS				
Time				
Money				
People				
Other				
OUTPUT TO BUSINESS PLAN				
Text	Process description			
Evidence	Market research			
Numbers	Resource implications - as above; Credit terms agreed with suppliers			

NOTE: All exercises and forms are available for download and completion at **www.growingabusinessinireland.com**.

SPOTcheck®
Score for this Factor

IMMEDIATE ACTIONS

OBJECTIVE
- To understand the impact of product development/ innovation on the growth potential of the business
- To identify appropriate interventions to eliminate weaknesses and to build on strengths
- To understand the importance of innovation
- To define targets, actions and the resource implications of these
- To draft text for the business plan

ANALYSIS

Innovation does not happen; it must be planned for, organised and managed. Do this exercise.

Innovation does not always have to be a "giant leap forward". It can be a small step or, better still, a series of small steps (the "continuous improvement" that is so much a part of Quality Management Systems).

The importance of innovation in the future is going to be even more significant due to constant change in technology, globalisation and the increased availability of information from the Internet, TV, computer, telephone and fax. To keep up with increasing competition, it is essential to be aware of those changes and constantly adjust the business to take account of new developments. Peter Drucker, the management guru, defined innovation as "*the purposeful and systematic search for change and opportunity*". To manage innovation, it is important to create a constant flow of information through the business. To do this, you need to set up an information system. This will bring together feedback from within your own business (for example, comments from your staff, clients and suppliers - all of which links with quality management) and combines it with

EXERCISE INNOVATION

Do you:
- Get constant feedback from and direct contact with customers (client panel)?
- Regularly review information from a wide variety of sources?
- Regularly hold brainstorming sessions with a group of people from different backgrounds?
- Have a budget for innovation?
- Make time for yourself or your staff to search for new ideas (for example, 3M allows R&D workers to spend 15% of their time on their own ideas and initiatives and has a rule that 30% of turnover must come from products developed in the last five years)?
- Have an "idea box" (like a suggestions box) with cash prizes if ideas are used by the business?
- Use project teams (made up of both technicians and sales people) to work with clients on specific ideas, with the team having the power and authority to implement necessary changes?
- Have a positive atmosphere in your business towards change?

EXERCISE PORTFOLIO OF IDEAS

Quantify how your commitment to innovation translates into product development:
> The number of ideas under consideration
> Their stage in the development process
> What action is planned to progress them
> Market potential of these ideas.

Innovation ...
endows resources
with anew capacity
to create wealth.

**PETER F
DRUCKER**

outside sources such as competitors, newspapers, trade magazines, etc. To prevent any restriction of vision, the information sources should be widespread and some should be unrelated to business - to help you keep an open mind. In this way, innovation links with the chapter on **Systems & Administration**.

R & D

Although research and development (R&D) is very often seen as relevant only to science and technology-based businesses, it is in fact applicable to all businesses, regardless of industry, market or size.

EXERCISE
RESEARCH & DEVELOPMENT

Is your product/service science or technology-based?   □ Yes □ No
Do you have specialist technical skills in this area?   □ Yes □ No
If "Yes", outline your qualifications.
If "No", outline how you propose to acquire the necessary technical skills.
If your product/service is not science or technology-based,
how have you arrived at your current design/definition?
How do you propose to keep your product/service up-to-date?
What resources does your R&D function require?

EXERCISE
TECHNOLOGY TRANSFER

Which areas of your business might benefit from technology transfer?
Have you identified a source of appropriate technology? □ Yes □ No
If "Yes", have you approached the source?   □ Yes □ No
If "Yes", with what result?
If "No", when/how do you propose to do so?
What benefit will the technology transfer provide you?
What is this worth to you?   €/£ _____
What is the asking price for this technology?   €/£ _____

TECHNOLOGY TRANSFER

Technology transfer is an "umbrella" term for a range of methods by which third parties can avail of ideas protected under intellectual property law. In your research, you may have identified a product/service, or process, that you believed had potential in your market. However, on further research, you discover that the idea is protected. Can you go any further?

Yes. You can approach the owners of the intellectual property rights that you are interested in and discuss the possibility of licensing those rights from them, or coming to some other arrangement. Usually, technology transfer is specific to a market (you would license the rights for Europe, or for your own country only) and a period (perhaps five years). The owners would share their protected information with you, enabling you to replicate their product/service, in return for a fee or royalty, usually calculated on the income you generate from the rights. Technology transfer is a complex area and you are recommended to take specialist advice.

Increasingly, universities are sources for technology transfer - most are keen to commercialise their own research, either directly through campus companies or indirectly through licensing and technology transfer.

INTELLECTUAL CAPITAL

Very often, intellectual property is seen as something for high-technology companies only. However, if you look at it in the context of managing knowledge, it quickly clear that it applies to almost all businesses - but especially to service businesses, whose most valuable assets "walk out the door each night".

In such businesses, intellectual capital - the knowledge contained within the business - is usually more valuable and more important to the business's success than the "hard" capital represented by whatever equipment the business uses.

Simply capturing the knowledge that exists within your business and sharing it can pay huge dividends and be a powerful engine of growth.

OUTPUT

Now that you have analysed the impact of the **SPOTcheck®** Internal Factor: **Product Development / Innovation** on the growth potential of your business, collate the results of your analysis. You will find this useful in **Section 4: Business Planning**.

EXERCISE
BEST PRACTICE

Have you ever identified "best practice":
> In your market sector?
> Among your competitors?
> Within your own company?

The only thing that keeps us alive is our brilliance.
The only thing protecting our brilliance is our patents.

EDWIN LAND

EXERCISE
KNOWLEDGE

Where is there knowledge within your business?
> Customer relations
> Patents
> Copyright
> Technology
> Operational practices
> Management practices
> Organisational arrangements
> Records and databases

How can this knowledge be shared to the advantage of the business?
Have you ever done an inventory of the knowledge contained within your business?

OUTPUT	Planning(now)	ThisYear	NextYear	YearAfter
TARGETS				
ACTIONS				
RESOURCE IMPLICATIONS				
Time				
Money				
People				
Other				
OUTPUT TO BUSINESS PLAN				
Text	Product idea portfolio; IPR protection			
Evidence				
Numbers	Resource implications - as above; Credit terms agreed with suppliers			

13: HUMAN RESOURCES

OBJECTIVE
- To understand the impact of human resources on the growth potential of the business
- To identify appropriate interventions to eliminate weaknesses and to build on strengths
- To define targets, actions and the resource implications of these
- To draft text for the business plan

SPOTcheck®
Score for this Factor

IMMEDIATE ACTIONS

ANALYSIS

As your business grows and more people are recruited, there is a greater need for specialisation and, in response, the business develops a more formal structure.

You must anticipate this and adopt a planned and systematic approach to recruiting, training and managing staff from the start.

EXERCISE
SKILL LEVELS

	Current skills	Planned requirement	Skill Gap

For each group of staff:
> What are their strong points?
> What are their weak points?

What areas do they need to improve on?
> Sales
> Finance
> Innovation/product development
> Production
> Marketing
> Management
> Communication
> Other (specify)

EXERCISE
FILLING SKILL GAPS

	Source	Cost

How will you improve your skill levels?
> Training
> Advisers/consultants
> Information system
> Recruit new staff
> Other (specify)

SKILL LEVELS

Earlier, you reviewed the skill levels of your management team. Now do the same for your staff, in the exercise below, breaking them into whatever groupings seem appropriate. Pay particular attention to the skills that the business will require in the future.

Next, in the exercise on the next page, examine how any skills gaps can/should be filled.

STAFF NUMBERS

Throughout this section of the workbook, you have completed an Output Form at the end of each chapter. Within the form is a section relating to "Resource Implications: People" - how many new staff you need now to handle the planning, and then in the current year, next year and the year after to handle the growth you have planned. Accumulate this information now in the exercise to arrive at an assessment of staff numbers during your business' growth phase.

Next, turn this information into money terms.

Make sure that you allow for non-salary costs (National Insurance/PRSI, bonuses, perks, etc).

This information will be a critical input into your business plan (see **Section 4**).

EXERCISE
PLANNING STAFF GROWTH

	Planning (now)	This Year	Next Year	Year After
RESOURCE IMPLICATIONS: PEOPLE				
Factor 1: Environment				
Factor 2: Market				
Factor 3: Customers				
Factor 4: Direct Competition				
Factor 5: Suppliers				
Factor 6: Promoters / Management Team				
Factor 7: Strategy				
Factor 8: Marketing				
Factor 9: Sales / Promotion / Channels				
Factor 10: Products / Services				
Factor 11: Process				
Factor 12: Product Development / Innovation				
Factor 13: Human Resources				
Factor 14: Use of Financial Resources				
Factor 15: Financial Performance				
Factor 16: Systems & Administration				
TOTAL				

EXERCISE
PLANNING STAFF COSTS

	Planning (now)	This Year	Next Year	Year After
RESOURCE IMPLICATIONS: MONEY				
Factor 1: Environment				
Factor 2: Market				
Factor 3: Customers				
Factor 4: Direct Competition				
Factor 5: Suppliers				
Factor 6: Promoters / Management Team				
Factor 7: Strategy				
Factor 8: Marketing				
Factor 9: Sales / Promotion / Channels				
Factor 10: Products / Services				
Factor 11: Process				
Factor 12: Product Development / Innovation				
Factor 13: Human Resources				
Factor 14: Use of Financial Resources				
Factor 15: Financial Performance				
Factor 16: Systems & Administration				
TOTAL				

RECRUITING

Recruiting staff is a major stumbling block for many small businesses. It takes time and effort. But the results can have an enormous impact on your bottom line. Hire the right people, and you will have a strong staff who will move your company forward. But the wrong person will pull down morale, waste your time, and cost you more than just an extra salary.

The key steps are:
- Know what you're looking for
- Finding applicants
- Interviews.

KNOW WHAT YOU'RE LOOKING FOR

Before you begin looking for someone to fill a vacancy, you need to know what you're looking for. You should:
- **Create a detailed job description** - Write down the specific tasks you expect this employee to perform. Think about every detail. Then summarise and put the tasks in order of priority
- **Develop a list of skills required** - What skills are essential? What skills are merely desirable?
- **Decide whether there are other things you want?** - Specific educational background? Experience in a particular industry? What else is necessary for the person to develop in your company?
- **Think about personality** - You need people who share your vision and your standards.
- **Take a reality check** - Look at what you have written down. Which areas are priorities? Where are you willing to compromise? Will you get the person you want for the salary you are offering?

FINDING APPLICANTS

Requirements defined, you now need to find people to meet them. Here are some suggestions:
- **Look in your files** - A visible and successful company will have people writing in looking for jobs, even though no vacancies are being advertised. If any of these people look promising, make time to meet and find out more about them. Then, when you need a particular mix of skills, you may find the perfect candidate in your files already
- **Ask your staff** - Your own staff may know someone with the right skills whom they would be happy to recommend (for a bonus, perhaps). And they will come with a built-in guarantee, since they won't want to let down the staff-member who sponsored them
- **Ask around** - Ask everyone you know (including customers and suppliers) whether they know anyone they would recommend. Have some background information available on the job ready to give out
- **Advertising** - Make it clear what you are looking for and write the ad to attract candidates. But make sure you have the time to handle a deluge of responses
- **Use a recruitment agency** - A sensible route if you do not have the time or ability to screen applicants, but it can be expensive. Through their contacts, agencies can often find people whom you would otherwise not reach with an advertisement
- **Look on-line** - The World Wide Web has opened up a new set of places to post your job vacancy. These are best used for high-tech vacancies
- **Contact University/IT career offices** - They are always looking for

jobs for their graduates and will usually circulate your listing free of charge

- **Job fairs** - An opportunity to give your company some visibility and talk to a variety of candidates in an unpressured environment
- **Non-traditional workers** - Don't overlook older or part-time workers or those with disabilities - they can be very capable and committed.

Whatever route you choose, it is a good idea to insist that every candidate completes a standard application. Keep the form simple but make sure that you get all the information you need to decide whether a candidate has the skills you require for the specific position. Use the candidate's CV as a back-up.

MAKE A SHORTLIST

Before you start looking at CVs or application forms, write out again a summary of the main points you are looking for in a candidate. Screen quickly looking for these - and only these. Put all applications that do not meet these criteria into a separate bundle. If you want, review them later to see whether they include any candidates you might want to keep for your files. Otherwise, remove them from consideration immediately. Write to them to say that you will not be calling them to interview - from the candidate's point of view, it's better to get bad news than not to hear at all.

Concentrate on the ones that meet your criteria. Read them again more carefully. Look for little things: gaps in employment, jobs that don't quite fit a career path, hobbies that don't sit well with the personality type you are looking for, inconsistencies and even, if the job involves written communication, misspellings and poor grammar.

Make a shortlist. Decide which candidates you want to interview and contact them to arrange dates and times. Although interview candidates should do their own research on your business before coming for interview, it is helpful to include some background information on your business with the letter confirming the interview.

INTERVIEWING

When interviewing, you only have a short time to find out all you need to make an informed decision about investing in someone who should become an asset to your business.

Therefore:

- **Use an interview checklist** - Develop a list of points that you want to cover during the interview (see panel above)
- **Ask open-ended questions** - Avoid questions that can be answered "yes" or "no"; use questions like "Why did you like working in sales?", "What are your strengths and weaknesses?" or "Why are you leaving your current job?"
- **Ask unconventional questions** - See how candidates think (and how fast) by asking them questions they may not have prepared for. For example, "Why shouldn't all staff be paid the same?", "If you didn't have to work, what would you do with your time?"
- **Find out what's important to the candidate** - What is he/she looking for: growth opportunities, regular hours, training, new responsibilities? Will he/she finish the job or just clock-watch?
- **Listen** - Spend 20% of the time talking and 80% listening. The purpose of the interview is to help you learn about the candidates, not to talk about yourself
- **Interview more than once** - Use

Most companies spend more time picking out an office copier than a $40,000 employee. And look which one can cause the most damage.

CRAIG ABERLE, CEO, Microbiz

the first interview to find the top two or three candidates; use the second to make sure you choose the best

- **Involve other staff** - If you are particularly pleased with a candidate, let them meet some of your existing staff with whom they will be working. Get these staff-members' opinion
- **Check references** - Ask what the relationship between candidate and referee is. Confirm previous positions, responsibilities and achievements. Ask about working habits, ability to get along with others, problems, etc.

Be open with candidates. Tell them that you are interviewing others. Give them a date by which they can expect to hear from you - one way or the other. Keep to it.

THE JOB OFFER

You have already discussed the job offer with your ideal candidate at interview, before writing to offer the job - in some cases, you may make the offer at the interview and shake hands on a deal. Either way, you should write to the selected candidate and set out clearly:

- The job title and description
- The salary; how it is to be paid; and whether it includes overtime, bonuses, etc
- The normal hours of work
- Holidays
- Period of notice required on resignation/dismissal
- Grievance procedures
- Any other "house" rules.

Send two copies of this letter, both signed by you, and ask for one back, signed by the new appointee to signify their acceptance of the position on the terms offered.

DEPENDENCY ON KEY STAFF

First, let's define "key staff". It need not be the "usual suspects" - the super-salesman or the technology wizard. It might be someone quiet and unassuming on whom your business depends a great more than you realise - until you lose that person!

EXERCISE
KEY STAFF

Who is "key" in terms of:
Networking within the company?
Keeping a good atmosphere within the company?
Coming up with new ideas?
Having detailed product knowledge?
Having contacts across the industry at all levels?
Being asked for advice by other staff?

"Key" can also be interpreted in terms of a person's contribution to a team. Sometimes, team players are overlooked in favour of stars - but can you imagine having 11 Roy Keane's on the one team!

STAFF RETENTION

Staff are a key success factor in any business. Managing staff has implications in every part of the business as very often your staff will be responsible for implementing all the bright ideas you come up with. They can make or break your ideas. And, properly encouraged, they can produce bright ideas of their own. Therefore, a lot of time and thought should be given not only to considering whom you want to recruit but also how to keep your staff happy and productive. To see why this is important, consider the costs of staff turnover:

- **Loss of capacity:** There's no one there to do the work, until you find a replacement

- **Loss of knowledge:** All that the person has learnt, before joining and while with your business, is gone
- **Loss of experience:** All the experience the person had is gone
- **Loss of network:** All the contacts that the person had are gone - some other employer has these now (are they a competitor of yours?)
- **Loss of training:** All the training you gave the person is gone
- **Cost of recruitment:** You will have to spend time and money recruiting a replacement and may have to pay the new person more than the person who left
- **Cost of induction:** The new person will take a little while to settle in, during which time they are producing below expected output and a drain on the time of other staff
- **Cost of new training:** You may have to train the new person.

All this means that you want to keep staff turnover to a minimum.

EXERCISE
STAFF RETENTION MEASURES

What measures have you put in place to ensure staff retention?

CHOOSING ADVISERS

An owner/manager has to be a master of all trades. But, as your business expands, you may need to hire a consultant or specialist to assist in implementing a project or dealing with a problem that you are unable to solve on your own.

Choose carefully - a good consultant can add immeasurably to your business, while a bad one could cost you a lot of money with nothing to show for it. Ignore qualifications - they are necessary but not the basis for choosing a consultant. Look instead for experience. A good consultant will refer you to his/her previous clients. Ask other owner/managers whose opinions you value for recommendations.

Selecting the right consultant or adviser is difficult. Before deciding on taking on an adviser, you should formulate some selection criteria.

Things to consider are:
- The consultant's knowledge of your business area and your specific project/problem
- His/her experience as a consultant and entrepreneur
- His/her way of working (dedicated to you until the project is done/available as necessary?)
- Ethics/confidentiality (can you trust him/her?)
- Costs (how/when will you be billed?)
- Time-frame (can the work be done when you want?).

Develop a clear briefing of what you expect from the adviser and ask for several quotes before you decide which one you are going to deal with.

ACCOUNTANTS

For information or advice on accounting or taxation matters, you are advised to consult your accountant.

If you do not know an accountant, check the classified telephone directory or contact one of the following accounting bodies:
- Association of Chartered Certified Accountants
- Institute of Certified Public Accountants in Ireland
- Institute of Chartered Accountants in Ireland.

Any of these bodies will be happy to put you in touch with one of their members close to where you live/work. Ask other entrepreneurs whose opinions you value

Accountants and lawyers make great accountants and lawyers. We need them, but we make the business decisions.
ESTEE LAUDER

for recommendations to their accountants.

Most accountants will not charge you for a first meeting. Use this to help you decide whether you want to engage the accountant or look further.

SOLICITORS

You need a solicitor to:

- Check out any lease, loan agreement or contract you may be asked to sign
- Advise you on relevant legislation
- Act as the final step in your credit control process
- Act for you if you are sued.

If you do not know a solicitor, check the classified telephone directory or contact the Law Society/Law Society of Northern Ireland for a recommendation.

HR MANAGEMENT

The quality of the HR management can be seen in two gaps:

- Between the current level of skills identified (see the chapter on **Promoters / Management Team**) and those needed for the future
- Between the current positioning of the company and its positioning statement.

How will you fill the gap(s)? The choices are set out in the exercise below.

OUTPUT

Now that you have analysed the impact of the **SPOTcheck®** Internal Factor: **Human Resources** on the growth potential of your business, collate the results of your analysis. You will find this useful in **Section 4: Business Planning**.

EXERCISE
PROCESS MANAGEMENT - FILLING THE GAP

The gap identified between current and future needs in process management is best filled by:

> Training the existing management team	☐
> Support from a mentor	☐
> Advice and guidance from a consultant	☐
> Recruiting a non-executive director	☐
> Recruiting an executive director	☐

OUTPUT	Planning(now)	ThisYear	NextYear	YearAfter
TARGETS				
ACTIONS				
RESOURCE IMPLICATIONS				
Time				
Money				
People				
Other				
OUTPUT TO BUSINESS PLAN				
Text	Product idea portfolio; IPR protection			
Evidence				
Numbers	Resource implications - as above			

SPOTcheck®
Score for this Factor

IMMEDIATE ACTIONS

FINANCIAL INFORMATION

In planning for growth, don't forget the need to support your core business activities with useful, timely and accurate financial information. For example, make sure that you have adequate:

- Records and clerical functions
- Accounts and wages systems
- Control systems to manage core activities such as purchases and sales.

You should also be preparing management accounts on a regular monthly basis. Quarterly accounts may have sufficed up to now but, in the intense period of growth that you are planning for, more up-to-date information will be needed to manage your business.

CURRENT FINANCIAL RESOURCES

What are your current financial resources? Complete the exercises below.

EXERCISE
CURRENT FINANCIAL RESOURCES - EQUITY

	Cash	Assets	Total£
Owner(s)			
External			
TOTAL			

OBJECTIVE

- To understand the impact of financial resources on the growth potential of the business
- To identify appropriate interventions to eliminate weaknesses and to build on strengths
- To understand how private equity can assist the growth process
- To define targets, actions and the resource implications of these
- To draft text for the business plan

EXERCISE
CURRENT FINANCIAL RESOURCES - DEBT

	Type	Amount	Interest rate %	Repayments	Source
Owner(s) loans					
Overdraft					
Term loan					
Long-term loans					
Mortgage on property					
Leases					
TOTAL					

The Lord forbid that I should be out of debt, as if, indeed, I could not be trusted.

FRANCOIS RABELAIS

EXERCISE
CURRENT FINANCIAL RESOURCES - SUBSIDIES

Subsidies	1	2	3	4
Source				
Subsidy type				
Subsidy value				
Conditions				
Timing of receipt				
TOTAL				

EXERCISE
FINANCIAL RESOURCES REQUIRED

	Planning (now)	This Year	Next Year	Year After
RESOURCE IMPLICATIONS: MO NEY				
Factor 1: Environment				
Factor 2: Market				
Factor 3: Customers				
Factor 4: Direct Competition				
Factor 5: Suppliers				
Factor 6: Promoters / Management Team				
Factor 7: Strategy				
Factor 8: Marketing				
Factor 9: Sales / Promotion / Channels				
Factor 10: Products / Services				
Factor 11: Process				
Factor 12: Product Development / Innovation				
Factor 13: Human Resources				
Factor 14: Use of Financial Resources				
Factor 15: Financial Performance				
Factor 16: Systems & Administration				
TOTAL				

FINANCIAL RESOURCES REQUIRED

Throughout this section of the workbook, you have competed an **Output Form** at the end of each chapter. Within the form is a section relating to **"Resource Implications: Money"** - how much you think it will cost to implement your growth plans in that particular section of your business. Accumulate this information now to arrive at an assessment of the financial resources you are likely to require in your business' growth phase. This information will be a critical input into your business plan (see **Section 4**).

RESOURCING STATEMENT

A resourcing statement sets out three things:

- What your current resources (cash, assets, people, intangibles, etc) are.
- What constraints you currently face (lack of investment, pressure on directors' time, etc).
- What resources you need to implement your growth strategy.

You are now in a position to write a draft resourcing statement for your business - it may change as you finalise your plan and succeed (or fail) in raising the necessary funding for growth.

Revisit the chapter on **Strategy** earlier in this section of the workbook and consider your resourcing statement in the context of the other statements you prepared there (and vice versa).

TYPES OF FINANCE

There are basically only two types of finance:

- **Equity** - Capital invested in the business, usually not repayable until the business closes down finally
- **Debt** - Capital lent to the business, usually repayable at a specified date.

There are also only two sources:

- Your own money
- Someone else's money.

EQUITY FINANCE

Private equity is increasingly available to help growth-oriented companies to succeed. The term "private equity" refers to venture capital as well as financing from individual investors, or business angels, who will provide an injection of cash to the business in exchange for equity or an ownership stake in the business.

Such investors are looking for a long-term return on investment, normally over a three to five-year period, and will therefore be expecting their equity stake to grow in value accordingly as the business grows. Private equity capital is often used by companies in different phases of growth and thus is often known as seed capital, start-up capital, early-stage capital and expansion capital. Private equity is also used for management buy-ins (MBIs), management buy-outs (MBOs) and company rescues or turnarounds, where a cash injection is required and there is a potential good return of investment for the investor.

Before you approach a private equity investor, you need to clarify some things in your own mind. Use the next exercise to help you.

	SOURCE	
TYPE	**Owner's**	**External**
Equity	Share capital	Share capital
Debt	Directors' loans	Overdraft, Bank loanLeasing, etc

**EXERCISE
PRIVATE EQUITY**

How much investment does your business need?

What will it use this investment for?

What is the current value of your business?

Hard assets - see conventional balance sheet

Soft assets - consider the value of:

> Brands

> Customer database

> Intellectual capital

> Human capital

Quality of strategic business plan

What are you willing to give?

> Equity shareholding

> Board memberships

What do you expect to get in return?

> Cash

> Experience

> Contacts

> Other (specify)

Who is going to negotiate with the investors?

What is our exit strategy?

Is our current plan good enough to submit to investors?

Guaranteed private equity finance investor turn offs include:
- *Flashy, expensive cars*
- *Personalised number plates*
- *Fountain in the forecourt or foyer*
- *Fish tank in board room*
- *Founder's statue in reception*
- *"We have no competition"*
- *"Microsoft will sign our deal next week"*
- *"All we have to do is get 1% of the market"*
- *"Our projections are conservative".*

CAROLINE MCGORAN, Enterprise Equity Capital Group

The benefit of private equity finance is that it is not a loan, but a cash injection into your business. In return the investors get shares in your company. The trade-off for selling some part of the ownership of the business to an investor is:

- Credibility (not everybody gets venture capital)
- Cash flow (an immediate boost to your cash resources, with the opportunity usually to seek additional funding when needed)
- Discipline (external investors impose a new level of discipline in decision-making and reporting on most businesses)

- Focus (again, external investors often see things more clearly than directors with day-to-day responsibilities)
- Management capability through a non-executive director (most private equity investors will expect a seat on your board)
- Business partners with the company's interest at heart (it's critical that the chemistry is right here)
- Accelerated growth (the purpose and bottom-line benefit of private equity finance).

A private equity investor will look at all the issues addressed in this workbook and in **SPOTcheck®**, starting with the management team and the business leader (the person capable of negotiating the deal with the equity providers).

The second criteria is the quality of the business plan (see **Section 4**). What is important in the context of private equity is the exit strategy, which needs to be clear from the start.

Once you have decided to go down the route of sharing ownership in return for cash in order to achieve growth, you will have to accept that you are accountable to your co-investors. Not being able to implement your plan and missing targets in sales, cost control, cash, technical development, etc. will create problems between you and your new investors. So think carefully about your ability to deliver. This is what the private equity investor will be trying to size up when they meet you - once they are on the team, they'll be able to see clearly for themselves.

Don't disappoint.

DEBT FINANCE

Debt finance includes:

* **Overdraft** - The simplest form of bank finance. Basically, this is no more than permission to have a minus balance on your bank account. However, overdrafts must be cleared (and stay cleared for at least 30 days during the year, though not necessarily consecutive days) on an annual basis and the overdraft is repayable on demand

* **Term loan** - A loan for a fixed period, usually at a variable rate. Repayments include interest and capital

* **Long-term loans** - Sometimes subsidised by Government or EU schemes, these aim to provide businesses with capital for 7 to 10 years

* **Mortgages** - Loans to buy business property, secured on the property itself, with fixed or variable rate options

* **Leasing** - A way of acquiring the use of fixed assets (for example, plant and machinery, cars, office equipment) by paying a regular monthly or quarterly payment, which is usually allowable for tax purposes. At the end of the lease, depending on the terms, you may have the option to continue using the asset for a small continuing payment or to buy it outright from the lessor

* **Invoice discounting** - A facility linked directly to sales, which maximises the cash value of current assets. The bank will pay you, say, 80% of the facc value of an invoice when it is issued. The balance, less charges, will be paid to you when the invoice is paid. Useful for the company that is expanding and in danger of being choked for lack of cash.

When considering financing your business with debt, you must consider:

* Fixed or floating
* Long-term or short-term.

Fixed debt is a loan that is secured on a specific asset - for example, on premises. Floating debt is secured on assets that change regularly - for example, debtors.

"Secured" means that, in the event that the loan is not repaid, the lender can appoint a "receiver" to sell the asset on which the loan is secured in order to recover the amount due. Thus, giving security for a loan is not something to be done lightly.

Because you have to pay interest on debt, you should try to manage with as little as possible. However, few businesses get off the ground without putting some form of debt on the balance sheet. The issues are usually:

* What is the cheapest form of debt available?
* What is the right balance between debt and equity?
* How to reduce the amount of borrowing required?
* Will borrowing be backed by personal assets?

It is a good idea to try to match the term of the loan to the type of asset that you are acquiring:

* To avoid constant renewing/restructuring problems
* To ensure that each loan is covered by the break-up value of the assets in case of disaster.

If you're short, take a loan. Never ask for a small amount. Ask for what you need, and always pay it back, the sooner, the better.

ARISTOTLE ONASSIS

TYPES OF FUNDING - WHICH TYPE IS MOST SUITABLE FOR YOUR BUSINESS?

FUNDING TYPE	Advantages	Disadvantages	Comment
External Equity	Long-term Suitable for funding property and equipment purchases No profit impact No repayment	Some loss of control Will require significant growth in business to justify investment (not suited to "lifestyle" businesses Sometimes difficult to raise in small amounts	Ideal if you can get it Make this your first choice, if you can live with loss of control and value safety over risk
External Loans	Can be split between long-term and short-term or overdraft to suit need	Interest will impact profit Must be repaid	Check Interest cover ratio Reschedule repayments to suit business' cashflow
Leases	Suitable for equipment purchases Offers an additional line of credit May give tax advantages	Interest will impact profit May be more expensive than bak borrowings Fixed repayments may not suit business' cashflow	Use for equipment where bank borrowings are not available
Subsidies	Often non-repayable	May have conditions attached	Worth looking out for, if available

SOURCES OF FINANCE

There is a wide range of sources of finance available to businesses that are expanding.

As these, and the availability of funds from them, change rapidly, this information is available on the website, **www.growingabusinessinireland.com**, where it will be updated regularly.

Don't overlook credit terms from your suppliers as a source of finance.

FINANCIAL MANAGEMENT

The quality of the company's financial management can be seen in two gaps:

- Between the current level of skills identified (see chapter on **Promoters / Management Team**) and those needed for the future
- Between the current positioning of the company and its positioning statement.

How will you fill the gap(s)? The choices are set out in the exercise below.

OUTPUT

Now that you have analysed the impact of the **SPOTcheck®** Internal Factor: Use of **Financial Resources** on the growth potential of your business, collate the results of your analysis. You will find this useful in **Section 4: Business Planning**.

EXERCISE
PROCESS MANAGEMENT - FILLING THE GAP

The gap identified between current and future needs in process management is best filled by:

> Training the existing management team	☐
> Support from a mentor	☐
> Advice and guidance from a consultant	☐
> Recruiting a non-executive director	☐
> Recruiting an executive director	☐

OUTPUT	Planning(now)	ThisYear	NextYear	YearAfter
TARGETS				
ACTIONS				
RESOURCE IMPLICATIONS				
Time				
Money				
People				
Other				

OUTPUT TO BUSINESS PLAN	
Text	Resourcing statement
Evidence	
Numbers	Resource implications - as above

NOTES

OBJECTIVE
- To understand the impact of financial management on the growth potential of the business
- To identify appropriate interventions to eliminate weaknesses and to build on strengths
- To understand how to calculate and use financial ratios
- To define targets, actions and the resource implications of these
- To draft text for the business plan

SPOTcheck®
Score for this Factor

IMMEDIATE ACTIONS

ANALYSIS

Your success in the financial management of your business is most easily seen in the financial ratios that can be generated from your accounting statements.

You can measure ratios for your own business against the same ratios for similar businesses or against ratios for your own business over a period of time. Use the exercises below to calculate the different types of ratios for your business:

- Profitability ratios
- Liquidity ratios
- Return on investment ratios
- Gearing ratios.

In addition, some businesses should calculate so-called "new economy" ratios, such as "cash burn rate", where these are relevant and informative.

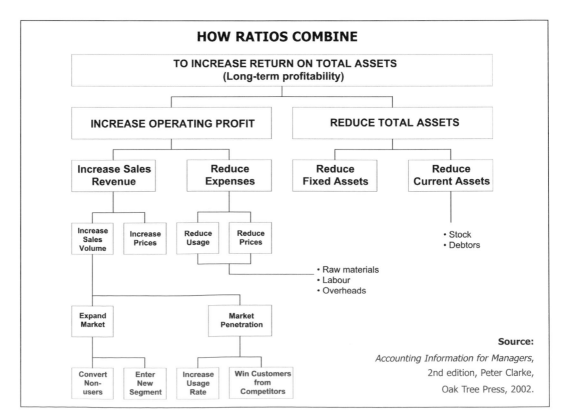

HOW RATIOS COMBINE

Source:
Accounting Information for Managers, 2nd edition, Peter Clarke, Oak Tree Press, 2002.

PROFITABILITY RATIOS

These ratios answer the question: "*How profitable is my business?*".

The two main ratios are:
- Gross profit: Sales
- Net profit: Sales.

There are also subsidiary ratios:
- Purchases: Sales
- Overheads: Sales.
- Gross profit: Sales

Details of how to calculate and use these (and the following) ratios appear in the **Appendix** to this workbook.

LIQUIDITY RATIOS

These ratios answer the question: "*How easily will my business generate cash?*".

They show the ability of the business to meet its day-to-day financial commitments by comparing the money it can expect to take in and pay out in the short term, based on the balance sheet position at the time the ratio is calculated.

The two main ratios are:
- Current ratio
- Quick ratio.

There are also subsidiary ratios:
- Debtor days - How long it takes your debtors to pay you
- Creditor days - how long you take to pay your suppliers
- Stock turnover days - how long it takes for your inventory to recycle.

RETURN ON INVESTMENT RATIOS

These ratios answer the question: "*What return does my business provide to investors?*".

They measure the effectiveness of a business in using the assets it employs. Because assets require funding, any surplus assets tie up capital that could be invested elsewhere to earn additional income. Therefore, a business should aim to minimise the assets it owns.

The main return on investment ratios are:
- Net profit: Total assets (Return on Investment - ROI)
- Net profit: Capital employed (Return on Capital Employed - ROCE).

The subsidiary ratios are:
- Sales: Total assets
- Sales: Fixed assets
- Sales: Current assets.

GEARING RATIOS

These ratios answer the question: "*Does the capital structure give me control of my business?*".

They look at the dependence of the business on outside funds and can give important indicators of loss of effective control by management to external providers of funding.

The main gearing ratios are:
- Debt: Equity ratio
- Equity: total assets.

A subsidiary ratio is the Interest cover ratio.

SUMMARY OF RATIOS

Use the exercise on the next page to summarise the ratios for your business in order to analyse where you might take action.

Learn to make numbers talk! They will speak to you about hard truths and also reveal the future!

JOHN D ROCKEFELLER

EXERCISE
RATIO ANALYSIS

Record the ratios you have calculated for your business. Compare them to an acceptable local norm. Identify the ratios that require improvement.

RATIO	Actual	Norm/Target	Difference	AcceptY/N?	Take ActionY/N?
Profit/(Loss) ratios					
Gross profit : Sales %					
Net Profit : Sales %					
Net Purchases : Sales %					
Overheads : Sales %					
Liquidity ratios					
Current ratio (times)					
Quick ratio (times)					
Stock Turnover (days)					
Debtor days					
Creditor days					
Investment ratios					
Net Profit: Total Assets %					
Net Profit : Capital Employed %					
Sales : Total Assets (times)					
Sales : Fixed Assets (times)					
Sales : Current Assets (times)					
Gearing ratios					
Debt : Equity %					
Equity : Total Assets %					
Net Profit : Interest (times)					

What you measure is what you get.

ROBERT S KAPLAN and DAVID P NORTON, Nolan, Norton, The Balanced *Scorecard*

Ratios are widely used by bankers who have access to comparative information for past periods of a business or for similar businesses in specific industries. Ratio analysis is also a useful tool for business managers when they have access to comparative data.

OUTPUT

Now that you have analysed the impact of the **SPOTcheck®** Internal Factor: **Financial Performance** on the growth potential of your business, collate the results of your analysis. You will find this useful in **Section 4: Business Planning**.

OUTPUT	Planning(now)	ThisYear	NextYear	YearAfter
TARGETS				
ACTIONS				
RESOURCE IMPLICATIONS				
Time				
Money				
People				
Other				
OUTPUT TO BUSINESS PLAN				
Text				
Evidence				
Numbers	Resource implications - as above			

NOTES

OBJECTIVE
- To understand the impact of systems and administration on the growth potential of the business
- To identify appropriate interventions to eliminate weaknesses and to build on strengths
- To define targets, actions and the resource implications of these
- To draft text for the business plan

SPOTcheck®
Score for this Factor

IMMEDIATE ACTIONS

INFORMATION

Information is becoming more and more valuable - and its value is being recognized more and more. In many cases, "soft" assets like information are more valuable than all the "hard" assets of a business, like computers, machinery, etc, put together - and more critical to the growth of the business.

The next point to consider is how well your business uses technology to support its information systems.

**EXERCISE
TECHNOLOGY UNDERPINNING
INFORMATION SYSTEM**

List the technology your business uses:
> Software
> Hardware
> Internet
> Intranet
> Filing systems
> Accounting systems
To what extent are these all integrated?

**EXERCISE
INFORMATION**

How well is your information system geared towards:
> Measuring soft capital?
> Capturing your intellectual capital?

INFORMATION SYSTEMS

Keeping informed on what is happening outside your business is difficult and you can be snowed under with too much information very quickly. But the outside world is where you sell your products/services and it is where the opportunities for growth lie, particularly in a world that is becoming more and more competitive.

The obvious sources of information on the outside world are the ones that you used earlier in your market research. Analyse which sources you should use on a regular basis in the exercise below.

Next, consider your "bandwidth".

**EXERCISE
SOURCES OF INFORMATION**

	Current	Planned
Which trade magazines are you subscribed to?		
How are you kept informed of international developments?		
What are the addresses of useful web sites?		
What are the trade organisations that you should join?		
Who are the people in your network who can keep you aware of developments?		
How do staff use the system and when?		
How is information presented for use?		

<table>
<tr><td colspan="2">

EXERCISE
BANDWIDTH

How wide is the "bandwidth" of your external information system?

Does it cover:

Technology?

People?

Economic sectors?

> Agriculture

> Banking

> Construction

> Education

> Government

> Hospitality

> IT

> Utilities

> Media

> Medicine/Health

> Military

> Retail

> Telecommunications

> Trade

> Transportation

</td></tr>
</table>

Information on what is happening within your business is just as important as knowing what is happening outside. Your internal information links all of the areas covered by the **SPOTcheck®** Factors. In each of the areas, especially those that are important to your business' growth potential, you should have metrics - quantifiable information that measures performance - for example, how many new orders were received, how many days stock is on hand, how much wastage of raw materials occurs, etc.

Use this exercise to explore your internal information systems.

OUTPUT

Now that you have analysed the impact of the **SPOTcheck®** Internal Factor: **Systems & Administration** on the growth potential of your business, collate the results of your analysis. You will find this useful in **Section 4: Business Planning**.

EXERCISE
INFORMATION FOR YOUR BUSINESS

What type of information do you need across the following functions:

	Importance	Frequency	Source	Who is responsible?	Metrics
BUYING					
Internal					
Inventory levels					
Re-order levels					
Delivery speed					
Response time					
Logistical costs per unit					
Vendor rating					
External					
Feedback from suppliers					
MAKING					
Internal					
Productivity					
Material usage					
Use of equipment					
Wastage					
Use of capacity					
Quality control problems					
% Defaults					
SELLING					
Internal					
Number of customers					
Number of repeat orders					
Sales expense in % of sales					
Journey planning					
Order size					
Sales funnel					
Call volume					
Price per lead					
Price per converted lead					
Sales per distributor					
Average call time per customer					
% success rate					
Discounts given					
Response time					
New contacts					
External					
Competition					
Market					
Economy					
Society					
Feedback from customers					
Stake holders					
Colleagues					
R&D					
Internal					
Number of improvements					
Number of new ideas					
Customer feedback					
Supplier feedback					
External					
Technological developments					
New product introductions					

OUTPUT	Planning(now)	ThisYear	NextYear	YearAfter
TARGETS				
ACTIONS				
RESOURCE IMPLICATIONS				
Time				
Money				
People				
Other				

OUTPUT TO BUSINESS PLAN	
Text	Description of information systems - internal and external
Evidence	
Numbers	Resource implications - as above

NOTES

The point has already been made that the **SPOTcheck®** Internal Factors all interlink and are mutually dependent.

Based on the "weakest link" principle, the management team's aim should be to eliminate weaknesses in the Internal Factors before seeking to build on strengths. The management team itself lies at the core of the Internal Factors, since it is probably the most critical Internal Factor on which growth relies.

WEBS is an acronym for **"Weaknesses eliminated, build on strengths"**. As explained previously, there is no point strengthening already strong features within a business - as long as there are weaknesses, that is where the business will remain exposed to failure. Eliminating these weaknesses - removing the "weak links" - is essential before resources are expended on building on strengths.

Visually, WEBS can be illustrated as in the diagram below. Each of the **SPOTcheck®** Internal Factors radiates outwards from the **Promoters / Management Team**, who are at the heart of the business, creating a spider's web of links.

There are also many links between the various Internal Factors - not illustrated here to avoid obscuring the diagram. These combine to create a web, like a spider's web, of links and connections and mutual interdependencies - again, **WEBS**.

OBJECTIVE
- To understand the WEBS principle
- To define strategic options from an internal perspective

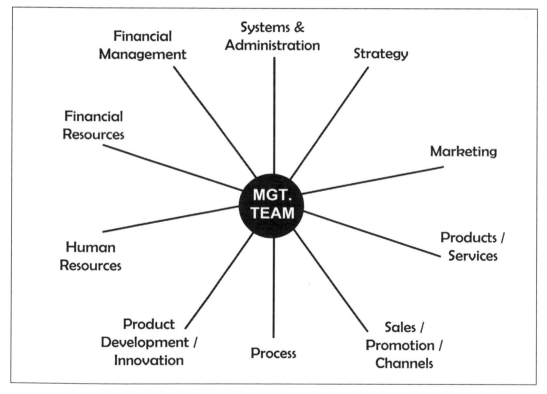

OBJECTIVE
- To understand how to develop a strategy from the work done to date
- To develop a strategy for the business

In some ways, strategy is never finalised. There's always new information coming to light that changes how you see the environment, customers, competition, etc. Nonetheless, there comes a point where you must (temporarily) draw a halt.

At this point, you can combine the strategic box, MOAT and WEBS that you have developed for your business into a single diagram that conceptualises in visual form your growth strategy. Look at how the diagram builds up below. Revisit the relevant chapters earlier in the workbook to refresh your memory on the meaning of the strategic box, MOAT and WEBS, if necessary.

When you overlay the individual elements on each other, you get the following diagram. Now you can see how the various elements connect.

The background represents the entire market environment.

The **MOAT** pentagon - defined by the **SPOTcheck®** External Factors: Environment, Market, Customers, Direct Competition and Suppliers - represents the part of the market environment within which the business operates. This pentagon is defined externally for the business and cannot be changed by the business. It offers opportunities and poses threats to the business. Accordingly, within the limits set, the business seeks to **"maximise opportunities, avoid threats"**.

The **WEBS** hexagon - defined by the **SPOTcheck®** Internal Factors: Strategy, Marketing, Products/Services, Sales/Promotion/Channels, Process, Product Development/Innovation, Human Resources, Financial Resources, Financial Management, and Systems and Administration - represents the elements within the market that are within the control of the business. Some are strengths, others are weaknesses. All are within the control of the business itself. Accordingly, its response to these Internal Factors should be **"weaknesses eliminated, build on strengths"**.

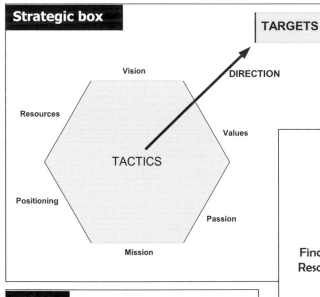

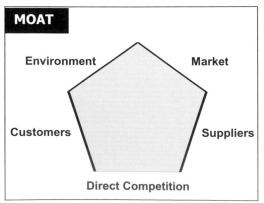

The **Targets** box represents the targets that the management team have set. The **Direction** arrow represents the overall thrust of the business towards achieving the Targets. The **Tactics** are the day-to-day activities that help the business move towards its Targets. And, at the heart of the diagram, linked to the WEBS, lies the management team.

Combining the strategic box, MOAT and WEBS represents visually the growth strategy of the business. It is a powerful way of grasping the concept of strategy. Understand this and you will have no difficulty in building a strategy for your business - or in applying it. Your path will be clear, your steps precise, and your aim true.

NEXT STEPS

Your next steps are to:

* Re-visit your six key statements: Values, Passion, Values, Mission, Positioning and Resourcing

* Re-visit the **SPOTcheck®** External Factors: Environment, Market, Customers, Direct Competition and Suppliers
* Re-visit the **SPOTcheck®** Internal Factors: Strategy, Marketing, Products/Services, Sales/ Promotion/Channels, Process, Product Development/Innovation, Human Resources, Financial Resources, Financial Management, and Systems and Administration
* Look again at your Management Team, its balance and composition, strengths and weaknesses in skills, etc. and how non-executive directors might help to grow your business
* Look again at your "soft" assets (knowledge, ideas and people).

Once you have done this, you are ready to tackle the next section of this **Growing Your Own Business** workbook - **Business Planning**.

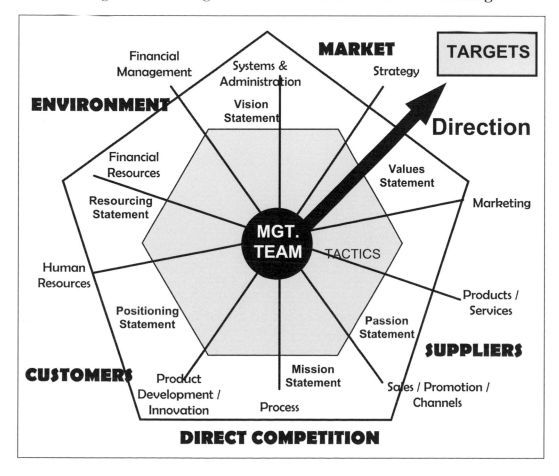

NOTES

SECTION 4: BUSINESS PLANNING

The process of business planning that you have just completed in answering the question **"How Do You Get To Where You Want to Be?"** in the previous section results in an output: the business plan document.

A business plan is a document that summarises the following points about your business:

- Where it has come from
- Where it is now
- Where it is going in the future
- How it intends to get there
- How much money it needs to fulfil its plans
- What makes it likely to succeed
- What threats or disadvantages must be overcome on the way.

This document can range in length from a few typed sheets of paper to several hundred pages. However, since professional readers of business plans - bankers, venture capitalists and enterprise officers - are offered more business plans than they can intelligently digest, the more concise your business plan, the more likely it is to be read.

The key elements of a business plan document are:

- **Text** - the narrative sections that make up the bulk of the plan
- **Evidence** - supporting evidence for all the assumptions and assertions contained within the plan - some of this is included in the Appendices, the rest is held available in case of query
- **Numbers** - the financial projections and some of the Appendices.

The text consists of a number of sections designed to introduce the reader to the business, recognising that they are busy, and making clear the funding need of the business (if that's the purpose of the plan).

Supporting evidence is often overlooked in the preparation of a business plan - only to be discovered when its absence is critical. Gathering supporting evidence during the process of business planning is recommended.

The numbers usually comprise the financial projections:

- Projected profit and loss account
- Projected balance sheet
- Projected cash-flow statement
- Other relevant supporting information.

Ike was right (see the quote in the margin). The quality of the planning you do for your business is critical to its success; how you document that planning process is less so. Nonetheless, a good business plan actively aids the planning process by providing a structure. It forces you:

- To cover ground that you might otherwise, in your enthusiasm, skip over
- To clarify your thinking - it is almost impossible to get your plan onto paper until you have formulated it clearly
- To justify your arguments, since they will be written down for all to see
- To focus on the risks and potential for loss in your plans as well as on the potential for profit and success.

Avoid unnecessary pessimism. Be realistic, but don't carry caution to extremes. If your growth strategy is realistic, have confidence in it.

OBJECTIVE
- To understand the process of business planning
- To draft a business plan

The plan doesn't matter, it's the planning that counts.

DWIGHT D. EISENHOWER, former US President

NOTE: All exercises and forms are available for download and completion at **www.growingabusinessinireland.com**.

If you have worked through the previous section, you already have a great deal of the information you need to write a business plan.

In this chapter, you will use the **Output Forms** from each chapter in the previous section to assemble the material from which you can write your business plan.

Once you have assembled the material for your business plan, then we can see what structure is used to create one.

EXERCISE
SUMMARISING OUTPUT FORMS - I

	Targets	Actions
Factor 1: Environment		
Factor 2: Market		
Factor 3: Customers		
Factor 4: Direct Competition		
Factor 5: Suppliers		
Factor 6: Promoters / Management Team		
Factor 7: Strategy		
Factor 8: Marketing		
Factor 9: Sales / Promotion / Channels		
Factor 10: Products / Services		
Factor 11: Process		
Factor 12: Product Development / Innovation		
Factor 13: Human Resources		
Factor 14: Use of Financial Resources		
Factor 15: Financial Performance		
Factor 16: Systems & Administration		
TOTAL		

EXERCISE
SUMMARISING OUTPUT FORMS - II

	Resource implications			
	Time	People	Money	Other
Factor 1: Environment				
Factor 2: Market				
Factor 3: Customers				
Factor 4: Direct Competition				
Factor 5: Suppliers				
Factor 6: Promoters / Management Team				
Factor 7: Strategy				
Factor 8: Marketing				
Factor 9: Sales / Promotion / Channels				
Factor 10: Products / Services				
Factor 11: Process				
Factor 12: Product Development / Innovation				
Factor 13: Human Resources				
Factor 14: Use of Financial Resources				
Factor 15: Financial Performance				
Factor 16: Systems & Administration				
TOTAL				

EXERCISE
SUMMARISING OUTPUT FORMS - III

	Business Plan		
	Text	Evidence	Numbers
Factor 1: Environment			
Factor 2: Market			
Factor 3: Customers			
Factor 4: Direct Competition			
Factor 5: Suppliers			
Factor 6: Promoters / Management Team			
Factor 7: Strategy			
Factor 8: Marketing			
Factor 9: Sales / Promotion / Channels			
Factor 10: Products / Services			
Factor 11: Process			
Factor 12: Product Development / Innovation			
Factor 13: Human Resources			
Factor 14: Use of Financial Resources			
Factor 15: Financial Performance			
Factor 16: Systems & Administration			
TOTAL			

EXERCISE
SUMMARISING
STATEMENTS

Values statement

Passion statement

Vision statement

Mission statement

Positioning statement

Resourcing statement

Your business plan must have a structure that is easily followed and understood by the person reading it. Although readers of business plans all look for different things in a plan (as we will see later in this section), there is sufficient overlap to be able to suggest a "standard" format below. Adapt this structure to your own needs.

A sample business plan format is available to download and print out from **www.growingabusinessinireland.com**.

BUSINESS PLAN - STRUCTURE

1. **Executive Summary** - 2-3-page summary describing the business, the product, the opportunity and the company's financial needs
2. **The Management Team** - Experience, skills, gaps
3. **The Products and Services** - what they are, unique selling points
4. **The Competitive Marketplace** - who are the competitors and potential disruptors
5. **Marketing Strategy** - how do you intend to get your brand known and your product into the target markets
6. **Design and Development Plan** - R&D effort and schedule to prepare the necessary products/services
7. **The Operations/Processes** - staffing, procurement, manufacturing, distribution, customer service, infrastructure
8. **The Financials** - financial needs, current and projected profit and loss accounts and balance sheets, projected cash-flow statements
9. **Appendices** - containing other information that may be of interest to the investors.

EXECUTIVE SUMMARY

This is the first part of a Business Plan to be read - and the last to be written. Here, in less than a page, you summarise the key points of your plan. It's easiest if you can put them in bullet point, like this:

This Business Plan:
- Explains how XYZ Company came to be
- Describes the products you intend to make
- Describes the market
- Shows how you will reach that market
- Costs the products
- Includes profit and loss account, balance sheet and cash-flow projections
- Requests grant aid of €/£xxk, based on equity already committed of €/£xxk and loans agreed of €/£xxk.

This is the most important part of the business, since it's usually on this that a decision is taken to read further. Most business plans are rejected before the Executive Summary has been fully read.

TEXT

The text elements of the business plan are important in attracting - and keeping - the reader's attention. This is so whether the reader is a potential investor, a banker, a supplier or key member of staff.

In drafting the text element of a business plan, the entrepreneur should assume the attention span of a goldfish, a complete lack of imagination and a reader who has lots of other things to do and within which the business plan has little priority whatsoever. Most professional readers of business plans receive far more plans to read than they have time to do so. So they make snap judgements, sometimes based on no more than the physical impression given by the plan and perhaps a few minutes' reading.

Therefore, the Executive Summary, the first part of the business plan document to be read, should be the last to be written and should have a disproportionate amount of writing time lavished on it. That's what sells the plan - that's where the entrepreneur's attention must focus.

WRITING THE PLAN

There are three stages in writing a business plan:
- Thinking
- Writing
- Editing.

Good results without good planning come from good luck, not good management.

DAVID JASQUITH

A brief written presentation distinguishes the facts from the opinions, and is the basis of all decision-making.

EDWARD G HARNESS

Each is important but the most important is the first - thinking. Be prepared to spend at least 70 per cent of the time you have allocated to preparing your business plan in thinking. This is the time that you have spent in the earlier sections of this workbook, deciding on your growth strategy. Time spent here will not be wasted. Use this time to talk through your business with anyone who will listen; read widely, especially about others in your area of business; and avoid finding reasons why things cannot be done.

Writing can be done fastest of all. Use a word processor, if you can. You will need the flexibility it gives to edit the document later.

If you find it difficult to start writing on a blank page or computer screen, talk instead. Buy, or borrow, a hand-held dictating machine. Talk to yourself about your business. Explain it to someone who knows nothing about it. Get the tape transcribed and your business plan will be on the way.

Editing is the last task. Editing is an art. Some people are better at it than others, but everyone can learn the basics. Read through your draft business plan - aloud, if you find that helps. Does what you have written say what you want?

Start deleting. You will find that quite a lot can be taken out without doing damage.

When you are happy with your draft, put it aside for a day or two. Come back to it fresh and see whether it still makes sense. Edit again where it does not. And when it is right, leave it alone!

EVIDENCE

The missing link in most business plans is evidence. An entrepreneur who has diligently completed the process of business planning should be capable of producing and providing evidence that supports the targets, strategies, decisions and resulting text and financial projections that make up their business plan. All of it builds up into a **"Book of Evidence"** that supports the business plan document and provides immediate answers to queries raised by readers of the plan. Some of this evidence can be made available in the Appendices of the business plan itself; most will be held available until requested.

The figure on the next page shows the critical questions that readers of a business plan may ask and shows where the answers ought to lie within a business plan (using the traditional format) and what evidence ought to back up those answers.

NUMBERS

Ideally, the financial projections grow out of the process of business planning - the exercises through which the planning is done generating numbers for input into the projections. Where financial planning takes place separately from the process of business planning, the resulting numbers are rarely dependable.

Critical inputs are:

For the projected profit and loss account
- Sales (volumes or values)
- Costs of Sales
- Fixed overheads
- Variable overheads

For the projected balance sheet
- Fixed asset acquisitions and depreciation
- Inventory
- Working capital
- Financial structure of the business

For the projected cash-flow
- Credit terms - received and given.

From these, and an understanding of the business model, financial projections can be developed - to whatever level of detail and sophistication is appropriate. Smaller businesses can manage with single-page statements of no more than a few lines each, trading away loss of detail in return for ease of comprehension. Larger, more complex businesses require greater detail, often summarised into appendices.

Usually, three years' projections are prepared although, increasingly, venture capitalists and other frequent readers of business plans dismiss the later years' data as little more than conjecture. Nonetheless, the exercise of thinking ahead the financial consequences of actions is educational for the entrepreneur and/or management team.

In addition, it is usual to prepare a schedule showing the business' need for funding and the proposed sources of same.

FIGURE
CRITICAL QUESTIONS, ANSWERS AND EVIDENCE

Questions	Your answer should be backed up by external evidence ...	... or internal evidence
PROMOTERS Can you show that you and your colleagues are suited to this particular venture?		CVs Personal circumstances Commitment
ORGANISATION Can you show that you have completed all the relevant legal requirements to set up your business? Can you show that you have an appropriate organisational structure in place to manage your business?	Legal status Taxation Licensing Trade mark registrations and patent applications	Organisation structure Information systems
SALES Can you show where your sales will come from? Can you show that you will be paid as quickly as you expect? Can you show that you have established the resources and activities that will be needed to generate, handle and meet your projected sales and that you have a plan to put them into place?	Market research Letters of comfort/forward orders Market research Letters of comfort/forward orders (including agreed credit terms) Quotations for fixed assets required showing price, terms and availability Deeds or Lease to premises Evidence of compliance with planning and other legal requirements for premises External research showing availability of suitable staff	Marketing plan Promotion budget Credit terms Marketing Plan Promotion budget Order processing and other selling functions Production process Logistics/ Distribution Organisational structure Workload
PURCHASES Can you show that you can secure supplies when you need them and on the terms assumed?	Contracts or letters of comfort from suppliers specifying prices, minimum order quantities, and payment terms Supplier price lists	Purchasing function Credit terms
ADMINISTRATION Can you show that you have a realistic plan for the administration and running of the business?	Quotations for services referred to in your overhead budget	Administration Analysis of the overheads required to run the business
FUNDING Can you show that you have clearly calculated the funding required? Can you show that you will be able to finance your business as planned?	Letters confirming external equity, loans, leases, etc, if not already paid in Valuations of any assets you are transferring to the business	Break-even analysis Ratio analysis Sensitivity analysis What If analysis Financial projections "Ownership" of the financial implications of your business plan

PROJECTED PROFIT AND LOSS ACCOUNT

Appendix Table: Profit and Loss (Planned)

Pro Forma Profit and Loss

	Jan	Feb	Mar	Apr	May	Jun	Jul	Aug	Sep	Oct	Nov	Dec	2000	2001	2002
Sales	$162,000	$162,000	$162,000	$162,000	$162,000	$162,000	$162,000	$162,000	$164,000	$165,000	$167,000	$168,000	$1,960,000	$4,060,000	$5,260,000
Direct Cost of Sales	$33,100	$33,100	$33,100	$33,200	$33,200	$33,200	$33,200	$33,200	$33,400	$33,600	$33,800	$33,900	$400,000	$827,000	$1,069,000
Other	$0	$0	$0	$0	$0	$0	$0	$0	$0	$0	$0	$0	$0	$0	$0
Total Cost of Sales	$33,100	$33,100	$33,100	$33,200	$33,200	$33,200	$33,200	$33,200	$33,400	$33,600	$33,800	$33,900	$400,000	$827,000	$1,069,000
Gross Margin	$128,900	$128,900	$128,900	$128,800	$128,800	$128,800	$128,800	$128,800	$130,600	$131,400	$133,200	$134,100	$1,560,000	$3,233,000	$4,191,000
Gross Margin %	79.57%	79.57%	79.57%	79.51%	79.51%	79.51%	79.51%	79.51%	79.63%	79.64%	79.76%	79.82%	79.59%	79.63%	79.68%
Operating Expenses:															
Advertising/Promotion	$3,700	$3,700	$3,700	$3,700	$3,700	$3,700	$3,700	$3,700	$3,700	$3,700	$3,700	$3,700	$44,400	$65,000	$70,000
Sales	$4,900	$4,900	$4,900	$4,900	$4,900	$4,900	$4,900	$4,900	$4,950	$5,000	$5,100	$5,250	$59,500	$70,000	$80,000
Miscellaneous	$800	$800	$900	$800	$800	$900	$800	$800	$900	$800	$800	$900	$10,000	$10,000	$10,000
Payroll Expense	$52,920	$52,920	$52,920	$52,920	$52,920	$52,920	$52,920	$52,920	$52,920	$52,920	$52,920	$52,920	$635,040	$910,000	$1,000,000
Payroll Burden	$7,938	$7,938	$7,938	$7,938	$7,938	$7,938	$7,938	$7,938	$7,938	$7,938	$7,938	$7,938	$95,256	$136,500	$150,000
Depreciation	$833	$833	$833	$833	$833	$833	$833	$833	$833	$833	$833	$833	$9,996	$30,000	$40,000
Quality Assurance	$7,700	$7,700	$7,700	$7,700	$7,700	$7,700	$7,700	$7,700	$7,900	$8,000	$8,100	$8,200	$93,800	$104,000	$125,000
General & Administrative	$8,000	$8,000	$8,000	$8,000	$8,000	$8,000	$8,000	$8,000	$8,000	$8,000	$8,000	$8,000	$96,000	$124,000	$174,000
Manufacturing & Engineering	$10,800	$10,800	$10,800	$10,800	$10,800	$10,800	$10,800	$10,800	$10,800	$10,800	$10,800	$10,800	$129,600	$130,000	$175,000
Machining & Systems Building	$7,200	$7,200	$7,200	$7,200	$7,200	$7,200	$7,200	$7,200	$7,200	$7,200	$7,200	$7,200	$86,400	$100,000	$110,000
Miscellaneous	$4,500	$4,500	$4,500	$4,500	$4,500	$4,500	$4,500	$4,500	$4,500	$4,500	$4,500	$4,500	$54,000	$75,000	$105,000
Total Operating Expenses	$109,291	$109,291	$109,391	$109,291	$109,291	$109,391	$109,291	$109,291	$109,641	$109,691	$109,891	$110,241	$1,313,992	$1,754,500	$2,039,000
Profit Before Interest and Taxes	$19,609	$19,609	$19,509	$19,509	$19,509	$19,409	$19,509	$19,509	$20,959	$21,709	$23,309	$23,859	$246,008	$1,478,500	$2,152,000
Interest Expense Short-term	$417	$417	$375	$333	$292	$250	$208	$187	$125	$83	$42	$0	$2,708	$0	$0
Interest Expense Long-term	$2,500	$4,583	$4,583	$4,167	$4,167	$3,819	$3,819	$3,819	$3,472	$3,472	$3,472	$3,124	$44,997	$29,150	$12,470
Taxes Incurred	$4,173	$3,652	$3,638	$3,752	$3,763	$3,835	$3,870	$3,881	$4,341	$4,539	$4,949	$5,184	$49,576	$362,338	$534,883
Extraordinary Items	$0	$0	$0	$0	$0	$0	$0	$0	$0	$0	$0	$0	$0	$0	$0
Net Profit	$12,519	$10,957	$10,913	$11,257	$11,288	$11,505	$11,611	$11,642	$13,022	$13,616	$14,847	$15,551	$148,727	$1,087,013	$1,604,648
Net Profit/Sales	7.73%	6.76%	6.74%	6.95%	6.97%	7.10%	7.17%	7.19%	7.94%	8.25%	8.89%	9.26%	7.59%	26.77%	30.51%

PROJECTED BALANCE SHEET

Appendix Table: Balance Sheet (Planned)

Pro Forma Balance Sheet

Assets

Short-term Assets	Starting Balances	Jan	Feb	Mar	Apr	May	Jun	Jul	Aug	Sep	Oct	Nov	Dec	2000	2001	2002
Cash	$60,000	$262,717	$404,028	$443,313	$400,051	$391,197	$252,246	$240,098	$117,046	$83,137	$89,939	$98,262	$65,256	$65,256	$454,875	$1,434,084
Accounts Receivable	$130,000	$186,500	$271,450	$238,950	$238,950	$238,950	$238,950	$238,950	$238,950	$240,450	$242,650	$244,875	$247,075	$247,075	$511,798	$663,069
Inventory	$90,000	$132,400	$132,400	$132,400	$132,800	$132,800	$132,800	$132,800	$132,800	$133,600	$134,400	$135,200	$135,600	$135,600	$280,353	$362,391
Other Short-term Assets	$15,000	$15,000	$15,000	$15,000	$15,000	$15,000	$15,000	$15,000	$15,000	$15,000	$15,000	$15,000	$15,000	$15,000	$15,000	$15,000
Total Short-term Assets	$295,000	$596,617	$822,878	$829,663	$786,801	$777,947	$638,996	$626,848	$503,796	$472,187	$481,989	$493,337	$462,931	$462,931	$1,262,027	$2,474,544
Long-term Assets																
Long-term Assets	$100,000	$100,000	$100,000	$100,000	$100,000	$220,000	$220,000	$370,000	$370,000	$370,000	$370,000	$370,000	$370,000	$370,000	$570,000	$870,000
Accumulated Depreciation	$30,000	$30,833	$31,666	$32,499	$33,332	$34,165	$34,998	$35,831	$36,664	$37,497	$38,330	$39,163	$39,996	$39,996	$69,996	$109,996
Total Long-term Assets	$70,000	$69,167	$68,334	$67,501	$66,668	$185,835	$185,002	$334,169	$333,336	$332,503	$331,670	$330,837	$330,004	$330,004	$500,004	$760,004
Total Assets	$365,000	$665,784	$891,212	$897,164	$853,469	$963,782	$823,998	$961,017	$837,132	$804,690	$813,659	$824,174	$792,935	$792,935	$1,762,031	$3,234,548

Liabilities and Capital

		Jan	Feb	Mar	Apr	May	Jun	Jul	Aug	Sep	Oct	Nov	Dec	2000	2001	2002
Accounts Payable	$75,000	$113,265	$77,736	$77,775	$77,823	$181,848	$77,260	$207,667	$77,140	$78,376	$78,729	$79,398	$79,307	$79,307	$126,191	$162,860
Current Borrowing	$50,000	$50,000	$50,000	$45,000	$40,000	$35,000	$30,000	$25,000	$20,000	$15,000	$10,000	$5,000	$0	$0	$0	$0
Other Short-term Liabilities	$10,000	$10,000	$10,000	$10,000	$10,000	$10,000	$10,000	$10,000	$10,000	$10,000	$10,000	$10,000	$10,000	$10,000	$10,000	$10,000
Subtotal Short-term Liabilities	$135,000	$173,265	$137,736	$132,775	$127,823	$226,848	$117,260	$242,667	$107,140	$103,376	$98,729	$94,398	$89,307	$89,307	$138,191	$172,860
Long-term Liabilities	$50,000	$300,000	$550,000	$550,000	$500,000	$500,000	$458,300	$458,300	$458,300	$416,600	$416,600	$416,600	$374,900	$374,900	$208,100	$41,300
Total Liabilities	$185,000	$473,265	$687,736	$682,775	$627,823	$726,848	$575,560	$700,967	$565,440	$519,976	$515,329	$510,998	$464,207	$464,207	$346,291	$214,160
Paid-in Capital	$50,000	$50,000	$50,000	$50,000	$50,000	$50,000	$50,000	$50,000	$50,000	$50,000	$50,000	$50,000	$50,000	$50,000	$50,000	$50,000
Retained Earnings	$130,000	$130,000	$130,000	$130,000	$130,000	$130,000	$130,000	$130,000	$130,000	$130,000	$130,000	$130,000	$130,000	$130,000	$278,727	$1,365,740
Earnings	$0	$12,519	$23,476	$34,389	$45,646	$56,934	$68,439	$80,050	$91,692	$104,714	$118,329	$133,176	$148,727	$148,727	$1,087,013	$1,604,648
Total Capital	$180,000	$192,519	$203,476	$214,389	$225,646	$236,934	$248,439	$260,050	$271,692	$284,714	$298,329	$313,176	$328,727	$328,727	$1,415,740	$3,020,387
Total Liabilities and Capital	$365,000	$665,784	$891,212	$897,164	$853,469	$963,782	$823,998	$961,017	$837,132	$804,690	$813,659	$824,174	$792,935	$792,935	$1,762,031	$3,234,548
Net Worth	$180,000	$192,519	$203,476	$214,389	$225,646	$236,934	$248,439	$260,050	$271,692	$284,714	$298,329	$313,176	$328,727	$328,727	$1,415,740	$3,020,387

Financials prepared using **Business Plan Pro 2003 Premier** from Palo Alto Software, www.paloalto.co.uk and reproduced by permission.

PREPARING THE PROJECTIONS

Whether you use dedicated financial projection software, like Palo Alto Software's Business Plan Pro on which the Figures on these pages have been prepared, spreadsheets that you develop yourself, or paper-based models to develop your financial projections is immaterial. The important point is that you have devised a method of capturing within your financial projections all the information necessary to reflect your research and thinking throughout the process of business planning in the form of financial data.

Check back to make sure that your projections are complete.

PROJECTED CASH-FLOW STATEMENTS

Appendix Table: Cash Flow (Planned)

Pro Forma Cash Flow		Jan	Feb	Mar	Apr	May	Jun	Jul	Aug	Sep	Oct	Nov	Dec	2000	2001	2002
Cash Received																
Cash from Operations:																
Cash Sales		$40,500	$40,500	$40,500	$40,500	$40,500	$40,500	$40,500	$40,500	$41,000	$41,250	$41,750	$42,000	$490,000	$1,015,000	$1,315,000
From Receivables		$65,000	$36,550	$154,000	$121,500	$121,500	$121,500	$121,500	$121,500	$121,500	$121,555	$123,025	$123,800	$1,352,925	$2,780,277	$3,793,730
Subtotal Cash from Operations		$105,550	$77,050	$194,500	$162,000	$162,000	$162,000	$162,000	$162,000	$162,500	$162,800	$164,775	$165,800	$1,842,925	$3,795,277	$5,108,730
Additional Cash Received																
Extraordinary Items		$0	$0	$0	$0	$0	$0	$0	$0	$0	$0	$0	$0	$0	$0	$0
Sales Tax, VAT, HST/GST Received	0.00%	$0	$0	$0	$0	$0	$0	$0	$0	$0	$0	$0	$0	$0	$0	$0
New Current Borrowing		$0	$0	$0	$0	$0	$0	$0	$0	$0	$0	$0	$0	$0	$0	$0
New Other Liabilities (interest-free)		$0	$0	$0	$0	$0	$0	$0	$0	$0	$0	$0	$0	$0	$0	$0
New Long-term Liabilities		$250,000	$250,000	$0	$0	$0	$0	$0	$0	$0	$0	$0	$0	$500,000	$0	$0
Sales of other Short-term Assets		$0	$0	$0	$0	$0	$0	$0	$0	$0	$0	$0	$0	$0	$0	$0
Sales of Long-term Assets		$0	$0	$0	$0	$0	$0	$0	$0	$0	$0	$0	$0	$0	$0	$0
New Investment Received		$0	$0	$0	$0	$0	$0	$0	$0	$0	$0	$0	$0	$0	$0	$0
Subtotal Cash Received		$355,550	$327,050	$194,500	$162,000	$162,000	$162,000	$162,000	$162,000	$162,500	$162,800	$164,775	$165,800	$2,342,925	$3,795,277	$5,108,730
Expenditures		Jan	Feb	Mar	Apr	May	Jun	Jul	Aug	Sep	Oct	Nov	Dec	2000	2001	2002
Expenditures from Operations:																
Cash Spent on Costs and Expenses		$13,019	$8,935	$8,940	$8,945	$20,902	$8,880	$23,870	$8,867	$9,009	$9,049	$9,126	$9,116	$138,668	$224,124	$284,739
Wages, Salaries, Payroll Taxes, etc.		$60,858	$60,858	$60,858	$60,858	$60,858	$60,858	$60,858	$60,858	$60,858	$60,858	$60,858	$60,858	$730,296	$1,046,500	$1,150,000
Payment of Accounts Payable		$78,906	$115,946	$80,418	$80,458	$84,094	$184,512	$84,421	$210,327	$79,843	$81,091	$81,467	$82,133	$1,243,615	$1,968,233	$2,527,982
Subtotal Spent on Operations		$152,783	$185,739	$150,216	$150,261	$165,854	$254,251	$169,148	$280,052	$149,709	$150,998	$151,451	$152,107	$2,112,569	$3,238,857	$3,962,721
Additional Cash Spent																
Sales Tax, VAT, HST/GST Paid Out		$0	$0	$0	$0	$0	$0	$0	$0	$0	$0	$0	$0	$0	$0	$0
Principal Repayment of Current Borrowing		$0	$0	$5,000	$5,000	$5,000	$5,000	$5,000	$5,000	$5,000	$5,000	$5,000	$5,000	$50,000	$0	$0
Other Liabilities Principal Repayment		$0	$0	$0	$0	$0	$0	$0	$0	$0	$0	$0	$0	$0	$0	$0
Long-term Liabilities Principal Repayment		$0	$0	$0	$50,000	$0	$41,700	$0	$0	$41,700	$0	$0	$41,700	$175,100	$166,800	$166,800
Purchase Other Short-term Assets		$0	$0	$0	$0	$0	$0	$0	$0	$0	$0	$0	$0	$0	$0	$0
Purchase Long-term Assets		$0	$0	$0	$0	$120,000	$0	$150,000	$0	$0	$0	$0	$0	$270,000	$200,000	$300,000
Dividends		$0	$0	$0	$0	$0	$0	$0	$0	$0	$0	$0	$0	$0	$0	$0
Adjustment for Assets Purchased on Credit		$0	$0	$0	$0	($120,000)	$0	($150,000)	$0	$0	$0	$0	$0	($270,000)	($200,000)	($300,000)
Subtotal Cash Spent		$152,783	$185,739	$155,216	$205,261	$170,854	$300,951	$174,148	$285,052	$196,409	$155,998	$156,451	$198,807	$2,337,669	$3,405,657	$4,129,521
Net Cash Flow		$202,717	$141,311	$39,284	($43,261)	($8,854)	($138,951)	($12,148)	($123,052)	($33,909)	$6,802	$8,324	($33,007)	$5,256	$389,620	$979,209
Cash Balance		$262,717	$404,028	$443,313	$400,051	$391,197	$252,246	$240,098	$117,046	$83,137	$89,939	$98,262	$65,256	$65,256	$454,875	$1,434,084

OTHER INFORMATION

Sometimes, there's other numerical information that can be valuable in communicating your growth strategy to readers of your business plan - for example, economic data, etc. Usually, this information is best contained in an Appendix.

GRAPHS AND CHARTS

It can be very helpful to the quick understanding of financial information to present it in graphs or charts. Business planning and spreadsheet software usually includes this facility and it is straightforward to create graphs and charts. Use the facility to help communicate your strategy.

Graphs prepared using **Business Plan Pro 2003 Premier** from Palo Alto Software, www.paloalto.co.uk and reproduced by permission.

FINANCIAL GRAPHS

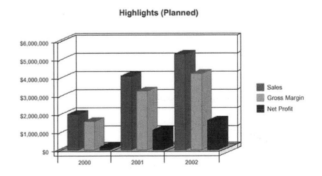

Highlights (Planned)

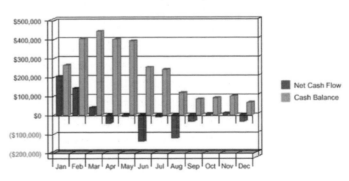

Cash (Planned)

Your business plan encapsulates your thinking and planning for growth. However, before you sign off on it, you should review it carefully.

FINANCIAL REVIEW

Start with a financially-directed review, to mimic the type of review that a banker or investor will carry out when considering the plan for lending or investment.

The techniques used to carry out a financial review of an almost-completed business plan include:

- Profit and cash-flow review
- Break even analysis
- Ratio analysis
- Sensitivity analysis
- Quantification of risk.

PROFIT AND CASH-FLOW

The aim here is to review both the profit and loss account and cash-flow projections for acceptability under normal investment criteria.

Ideally, one is looking for:

- Profit (or an acceptable level of losses, with profitability in sight) to be achieved within the period of the projections
- Positive cash-flow (or positive cash-flow in sight) within the period of the projections
- Explanations of sharp fluctuations in monthly profitability or net cash-flow
- Explanations for significant impacts on profit or cash-flow in specific months.

If you need to improve the projected financial position of the business, useful areas to consider are:

- **Sales** - can these be increased, whether in value, volume or mix?
- **Purchases** - can cheaper alternative suppliers or raw materials be found?
- **Credit terms** - both debtors and creditors.
- **Overheads** - can any be cut, reduced or postponed?

BREAK-EVEN ANALYSIS

Calculating a business' break-even point is an elementary, though often overlooked, review tool. The size of gap between current turnover and break-even turnover may be too great to be bridged and an alternative, less ambitious, growth strategy may need to be considered. In most cases, however, a small boost is all that is needed to get a business over the break-even hurdle point.

Areas to consider that affect the achievement of break-even include:

- **Sales price** - can this be increased?
- **Sales volume** - can this be increased?
- **Cost of sales** - can this be reduced?
- **Overheads** - can this be reduced?

RATIO ANALYSIS

Modern finance offers a wide range of ratios for calculation, including:

- Profitability ratios
- Liquidity ratios
- Investment ratios
- Gearing.

You have already considered these ratios in the previous section (see chapter on **Financial Management**) but should quickly review them again for anomalies. One can look at the ratios as a static analysis of the relationships between key figures within the projections and use them to measure the business against industry norms.

A more dynamic alternative links the relationships to key figures with the underlying business activity and suggests that, if the ratios are unacceptable, changes in the underlying business activity are required.

Thus, if a ratio is x%, when y% is

desired, then by identifying the underlying business activities whose relationship is reflected in the ratio, the management team can tackle bringing the ratio back into line. For example, the key drivers in a sales context include price, volume, product mix and seasonality.

So, one way of increasing sales income is to increase prices, which can be achieved inter alia by one or more of the following:

- Discount reductions
- Quality increases (real or perceptional)
- Changes in packaging (to justify a higher price)
- Design changes
- Changes to the manner of distribution.

Each of these has consequences, in terms of costs, or market perception or manufacturing, etc, and these consequences must be taken into account in deciding what action should be taken to bring the ratio to the desired level. But the ratios provide a means of working back dynamically to a desired performance, by altering the underlying business activity.

SENSITIVITY ANALYSIS

In any business, there are a small number of critical factors that have an undue influence on its success (or lack of it). For example, because of high fixed costs, a business may have a high break-even point, although once past that point profits flow steadily in. Such a business could be vulnerable to changes in market conditions that reduce turnover below the break-even point. Identifying these critical factors, and their impact, is sensitivity analysis.

Bankers and investors use sensitivity analysis to identify areas of potential weakness in a business plan: "*What would happen if ...?*". It is wise, therefore, to perform the analysis oneself - and wiser still to use it to develop a stronger business plan.

QUANTIFYING THE RISK

It is important for a management team to consider the risks to which they and their business are (or may be) exposed. With this insight, the plan can be adjusted to account for these exposures; without it, the business continues to be exposed without warning of likely incidence.

When the risks have been identified, the management team can:

- Reconsider the business plan and look at alternatives
- Review their insurance situation (personal and business)
- Review their dependency on particular customers, suppliers, or staff.

TEXT REVIEW

Finance has been used as the main driver of the business planning review process. But a management team should also look to the text of their business plan, to consider whether it fairly reflects their efforts at planning the development of the business.

In addition, a re-run of **SPOTcheck®** will always prove helpful.

The management team should aim to be able to answer the following questions quickly and easily from the business plan document - the questions reflect a reader's immediate concerns about the viability of the growth strategy and go to the heart of the business model. They are:

- Who are you?
- What is your (new) product or service?
- Who are your customers?
- Why will your (new) customers buy your product or service?

Even the best plan degenerates into work.

ANON

EXERCISE
REVIWING YOUR BUSINESS PLAN

A clear concise Executive Summary - The reader must know what the plan is trying to achieve and how it holds together

Figures - Clearly state assumptions

Business - An overview of how the business works is required. The quality of the business must be evident

Business model must be clear - How functional areas interact/support each to sell product/service

Product - Clearly defined and customer uses clarified. Competitive advantage must be evident

Sales - Based on firm orders, not letters of intent. Must be deliverable

Market information - Must be included to demonstrate growth potential

Industry overview - Show business in context. Show that business is a winner

Money - Where does business make its money? Pinpoint exactly

People - Note past achievements

Layout - Spaces, easy to read and get a handle on key messages.

EXERCISE
A REALITY CHECK

You have finished your Business Plan. You are ready to submit it to your bank or a potential funder. Before you do, run these final checks:

Is the Executive Summary:
> Short?   ☐
> Relevant?   ☐
> To the point?   ☐
> Interesting?   ☐
> Packed with "Ooomph"?   ☐

Check the entire Business Plan (get help if you need it) for:

Spelling mistakes - Use a spelling checker if your business plan has been word-processed   ☐

Grammatical mistakes - Use a grammar checker (but be careful) if your business plan has been word-processed   ☐

Page numbering - Are the pages all in order, with no gaps or duplication?   ☐

Chapter/section numbering - Are the chapters/sections all in order, with no gaps or duplication?   ☐

Cross-references between sections/pages - Are these correct?   ☐

Logical structure - Does the plan flow in a sensible order?   ☐

Jargon/use of language - Do you introduce concepts, explain jargon, demystify complicated things for the reader?   ☐

Length - Is it too long? Could you cut parts out, without damaging it? Could sections be moved into an Appendix?   ☐

Type size/style - Is it easy to read? Are headings clearly identifiable?   ☐

Colour - If you are using coloured type, does it help or does it distract? Keep it simple.   ☐

- What price will your customers be willing to pay for your product or service?
- At this price, how many products/services will your customers buy?
- How many products/services can you make?
- How much does it cost to make/deliver each unit of product/service?
- How much investment does the business need to achieve its growth strategy?
- Is this a viable business?

OVERALL REVIEW

Note that in reviewing your business plan, it is important to take an holistic approach, recognising that decisions made in one area may have impacts in other areas. For example, it is unlikely that sales can be significantly increased in the short-term without significant additional marketing expenditure or other costs. If the aim of increasing sales revenue is thus to boost profitability, account must also be taken of the negative profit effect of increased expenditure on marketing. And, next, the capacity of the production systems and the chosen channels of distribution need to be checked, to ensure that they can cope with the proposed increased sales volume - and so on, until the plan as a whole is back in balance again.

A FINAL REALITY CHECK

Your business plan is now almost finished - except that, just like your market research and testing of your product - you must test it.

Perform the Reality Check in the panel. Then give your business plan to a few trusted friends to read through. Ask them to pick holes in it. Don't be defensive. Use their comments to improve the plan.

Thus far, we have discussed a single "business plan document". However, in reality, there will probably be several different documents representing the business plan, across a spectrum from an operational manual to a fund-seeking document. Each document needs to be tailored both to its audience and its purpose.

The operational manual-type business plan document will be lengthy, detailed and effectively a turn-key manual for implementing the development of the business. It will show step-by-step how the management team plans to achieve its targets.

On the other hand, the fund-seeking document will be much shorter (perhaps no more than a dozen pages), will be focused on the reader's needs and will explain what funding is required, how it will be used, what results are expected and how the reader will benefit from investing in the business.

Thus, a business plan may have different audiences, each with different information needs, each with their own perspective, including:

- **The entrepreneur:** To manage the business
- **Management team and key staff:** To understand their roles in implementing it
- **Bankers:** To assess any loan applications you make
- **Investors:** To judge the risk/return potential of your business
- **Advisers to the business:** To let them quickly "read in" to your business strategies
- **Customers or suppliers:** You may circulate parts of the plan to important customers or suppliers, to gain their support.

As in any communication situation, the key to the style and emphasis of the document is determined by:

- Why does the person want to read the document?
- The level of detail they require to make a judgement
- The level of confidentiality needed and offered.

Again, the Executive Summary is critical. It must:

- Persuade this particular reader that the idea is good - knowing what your reader is looking for is key
- Summarise the company, its objectives, and why it will be successful in achieving growth
- Explain the growth strategy and how it will be implemented
- Describe the products, the market, and critical financial information
- Outline what finance is required - how much, in what form and when
- Assume that its reader is not expert in your industry and knows nothing about your business
- Be short and easy to read.

Where funding is required, the document must explain:

- How much is required
- How much the entrepreneur (and/or management team) has contributed
- How much has already been secured from other sources (identify them)
- How much is still to be raised and what form it is expected to take (equity, debt or subsidies).

Remember, the only objective evidence that an entrepreneur or management team can show at this stage is the thoroughness with which they have completed the business planning process - and this will only be communicated through the business plan document.

How a financier reads a business plan depends on what kind of financier he, or increasingly she, is. There are two types of financier - the lender and the investor.

The **lender** is typically your bank manager. Lenders will invest money in your business, if they think it worth doing so by their criteria, in return for interest on the capital. The **professional investor**, on the other hand, will invest equity in your business and share in your risk as owner of the business. Professional investors will postpone their return for a period - typically, three to five years - but will look for an above-average return for the risk involved in doing so.

THE LENDER'S VIEW

The average bank manager will be looking to see how you have handled, or propose to handle, the risks, particularly the financial risks, that your business is likely to encounter. Bank managers are concerned about the security of the bank's money - or more properly, the depositors' money - which you are seeking and for which they are responsible.

That is not to say that a bank manager will not back you. Most bank managers have discretion in the amounts they lend to businesses and will sometimes back their own hunches or gut feelings against the apparent odds. But do not bet on it. Turn the odds in your favour by writing your business plan and framing your request for finance in the best light.

Arnold S. Goldstein, American author of **Starting on a Shoestring** (John Wiley & Sons, ISBN 0-471-13415-5), suggests the following likely line of questioning from a bank manager:
- Why do you need the amount requested?
- What will you do with it?
- How do you know it's enough?
- How much less can you live with?
- Who else will you borrow from?
- How do you propose to repay it?
- How can you prove that you can?
- What collateral can you offer?

Unless you can answer these questions to your bank manager's satisfaction, it is unlikely that you will get the money you are looking for.

And don't wait for the interview with the manager for an opportunity to give the answers to these questions - that is far too late. The bank manager's mind will already be made up, more or less, before your meeting. Your plan will have been read thoroughly. The interview is intended to firm up the manager's decision. If you have not answered the relevant questions in the plan, you are not likely to have much chance to do so later.

You don't need to write your business plan in a style that asks the questions in the form above and then gives the answers. What you need to do is to ensure that the information that answers the questions is:
- Contained within the plan
- Visible within the plan
- Capable of being extracted by a reader from the plan.

WHY BANKS MAY NOT FINANCE GROWTH

Some of the reasons why banks will not finance a business idea:

Lack of research - Would you lend to a restaurant with a high dependency on passing traffic when you know a bypass is scheduled in a year's time?

Inexperienced management - The pub business is a classic example. Everybody fancies that they have the necessary expertise - not always so

Repayment capacity - Projections always show repayment capacity but the optimism of promoters is sometimes difficult to justify

No planning for setbacks - Most loan applications fail to recognise that real life does have setbacks.

Value of asset dependent on trading success - This is obvious but not always appreciated. It is particularly relevant in investment property but applies to most fixed assets (for example, machinery)

Grants & subsidies - Sometimes these mask the true viability (or lack of it) of an enterprise.

Make sure your Business Plan avoids these faults.

Putting all this in another way, a bank manager will look for three things:

- Character
- Collateral
- Cash-flow.

Character means you. A bank manager who has any reason to distrust or disbelieve you - from previous dealings or because of your reputation or because of errors or inconsistencies in your business plan - will not invest money with you.

Collateral means the backing that you can give as security for the loan. In some cases, collateral is not needed. But to the banker, who is responsible to the bank's depositors for their money, security is all. If you can offer collateral, it will certainly help your case.

Cash-flow means your ability to repay the loan on time, out of the proceeds of the investment. The bank manager will prefer to see the loan repaid at regular monthly or quarterly intervals with interest paid on the due dates - anything else upsets the system. Unless you can show that the business will generate enough cash to make the payments the bank manager requires - or you have explained clearly in your business plan why this will not be possible for an initial period - you will not get the money that you ask for.

PROFESSIONAL INVESTORS

Professional investors, venture capitalists or private equity investors for example, have a different viewpoint. They accept risk, though, like any prudent investor, they will avoid undue risk and seek to limit their exposure to unavoidable risk. Their questions will be along the lines of:

- How much can I make?
- How much can I lose?
- How do I get my money out?
- Who says this is any good?
- Who else is in it?

How much can I make? decides whether the project fits the profile of 30% to 50% annual compound growth usually required.

How much can I lose? identifies the downside risk. Although venture capitalists are used to risk, they cannot invest in projects that would jeopardise their own business in the event of failure.

How do I get my money out? is important since few venture capitalists invest for the long term. Most are happy to turn over their investments every three to five years. None will invest in a project unless they can see clearly an exit mechanism. There is no point in holding a 25% share in a company valued at several millions if you cannot realise the shareholding when you want to.

Who says this is any good? Professional investors maintain networks of advisers, often on an informal basis. Venture capitalists will check out all that you say or include in your business plan. This is part of the "due diligence" process. If you can supply a venture capitalist with evidence that those who ought to know support your plans, you will strengthen your case.

Who else is in this? panders to the investor's residual need for security. Even if investors know that they are going to take a risk, to place their faith and money in your hands, they like to know that others have come to the same conclusion. There is nothing like unanimity to convince people that they are right! Don't mock - particularly if you're trying to persuade someone to invest. Some venture capitalists have such a reputation for being right, for picking winners, that others try to follow their lead whenever they can.

THE PROFESSIONAL INVESTOR'S KEY AREAS

The market: Is it large and growing rapidly?
The product: Does it solve an important problem in the market?
Management: Are all the key functional areas on board?
Exit mechanism: How do I get my money out when this project succeeds?

There is no finish line.

NIKE motto

The business plan reflects all the changes in thought/direction since the management team started the process of business planning.

What appears in the business plan document is the end result of the process - the proof that the team has planned their growth strategy. But it's not the "final" plan.

A business plan must reflect the business. As it changes direction, so too must the business plan. The two are inextricably linked. Growth is not just a once off exercise - it's ongoing

That's why so much emphasis has been laid on the process of business planning, because a process is on-going. Business planning never ends. It's always happening and the business plan document needs to be reviewed and updated regularly as a routine part of the management of the business.

PROFITABILITY RATIOS

GROSS PROFIT : SALES

Gross profit / Sales X 100

This ratio is expressed as a percentage - for example, 47.5% - and shows management's ability to control selling prices, cost of sales and sales volumes. The higher this ratio, the higher the gross profit, and the more money is available to cover overheads and to allow for profit. Different industries have different gross profit structures. Some work on high gross profit margins, balanced by high overheads, while others have lower gross profit margins requiring them to run very tight control on their overheads. You can improve this ratio by:

- Increasing Sales income by increasing selling prices
- Reducing Cost of Sales by negotiating a lower purchase price for your products/services
- Reducing Cost of Sales by reducing waste
- Increasing the difference by including more of the more profitable products/services in your sales in the sales mix
- Reducing any Direct Overheads included in Cost of sales.

NET PROFIT : SALES

Net profit / Sales X 100

This ratio is expressed as a percentage - for example, 10.5% - and shows your overall performance in managing prices, costs of sales and all overheads to generate a return for the business. What constitutes good or bad results here depends on the type of business. Since Net profit is the difference between Gross profit and Overheads, the actions you can use to improve this ratio include those for the Gross profit ratio. You can also:

- Reduce Overheads
- Increase Sales volume.

NET PURCHASES: SALES

Net purchases / Sales x 100

This ratio is expressed as a percentage - for example, 22.7%. - and indicates the economies achieved in buying and inventory management while controlling selling prices. To improve the ratio:

- Renegotiate better terms with suppliers
- Seek out alternative suppliers
- Identify cheaper replacement materials or products, whose quality will not damage sales
- Reconsider redesigning the product/service
- Re-examine inventory policy and stores to eliminate waste.

OVERHEADS: SALES

Overheads / Sales x 100

This ratio is expressed as a percentage - for example, 15.5% - and indicates the level of performance in administering the business.

LIQUIDITY RATIOS

CURRENT RATIO

Current assets / Current liabilities

or

[Inventory + Debtors + Cash] / Current Liabilities

This ratio is expressed as a number - for example, 1.4, representing the number of times that current assets cover current liabilities. Current assets are expected to convert into cash within the next 12 months at least and current liabilities are expected to be paid within the next 12 months. Therefore, a ratio of 1.4 says that, based on the business' current financial situation, for every €/£1.00 the business is currently committed to pay over the next 12 months, it expects to receive €/£1.40 and would therefore not anticipate problems in meeting its obligations.

QUICK RATIO

[Debtors + Cash] / Current Liabilities

Overall liquidity is determined both by the funding structure used in your business. and by your business' profit margin.

Important measures of a business' skill and commitment in managing liquidity are:

- The rate at which it settles amounts due to suppliers
- The rate at which it collects amounts receivable from debtors
- The levels of inventory it carries.

These are measured by the following subsidiary liquidity ratios:

- Debtors days
- Creditors days
- Stock turnover.

DEBTORS DAYS

Debtors / Credit sales x 360

This ratio is measured in days and is used to indicate the performance in collecting amount receivable from debtors. Note that if the debtors figure includes VAT (or other turnover taxes), the figure for credit sales should include VAT also, to ensure that like is compared with like. Ideally, this ratio should be minimised, insofar as is consistent with the business' marketing strategy.

CREDITORS DAYS

Creditors / Credit purchases x 360

This ratio is measured in days and is used to show the average credit period taken by the business from its suppliers. Ideally, this ratio should be maximised, although a ratio that is higher than the industry norm might be an early indication of cash-flow difficulties.

STOCK TURNOVER

Inventory / Cost of sales x 360

This ratio is measured in days and is used to indicate the level of investment tied up in inventory and can be minimised by:
- **Reducing the minimum re-order value:** This means that you will re-order more often but in smaller quantities.
- **Buying more cheaply.**

RETURN ON INVESTMENT RATIOS

NET PROFIT/TOTAL ASSETS

Net profit / Total assets x 100

This ratio is often known as the Return on Investment (ROI), sometimes also known as the "Primary" ratio. It shows the profit generated by all assets used in the business. Obviously, the lower the cost of the assets, the higher the ROI for the same level of profit.

NET PROFIT/CAPITAL EMPLOYED

Net profit / Capital employed

This ratio measures the return on the long-term capital (owners' funds and loans) invested in the business and emphasises the goal of maximising return on investment.

SALES/TOTAL ASSETS

Sales / Total assets

The Sales: Total assets ratio shows the efficiency of management in generating sales from all the assets at their disposal. The determinants are effective use of productive assets such as machinery and tight control over inventory and receivables.

SALES / FIXED ASSETS

Sales / Fixed assets

This ratio is expressed as a number of times and is a subset of the Sales: Total assets ratio and indicates the performance in utilising the fixed assets to generate sales.

SALES/CURRENT ASSETS

Sales / Current assets

This ratio is expressed as a number of times and is a subset of the Sales: Total assets ratio and indicates the ability of management to generate sales while controlling debtors and inventory. These ratios are improved by actions that increase profit and that reduce unnecessary inventory and amounts receivable from debtors. You should also explore ways of reducing the levels of investment in fixed assets - for example, can you rent or lease rather than buy?

GEARING RATIOS

DEBT: EQUITY

Debt / Equity x 100

or

External loans / Owners' funds x 100

This ratio is called the Debt/Equity ratio and examines the structure of the long term capital used in the business (the "gearing"). When this ratio reaches 100% or more, lenders have as much money invested in the business as the owners, and a business is considered to be "highly geared". A highly-geared company can expect more difficulty in raising further loans and its profitability may be may be vulnerable to an increase in interest rates. This exposure of a business to changes in interest rates is measured by the Interest Cover ratio.

INTEREST COVER RATIO

Net profit / Interest

The Interest Cover ratio is expressed as a number and shows the number of times the interest payable on loans is covered by profit. It allows a banker (and you) to assess the affect of an increase in interest rates on the business' profitability. A low level of cover - say 1 to 5 - means that an increase in interest rates would significantly damage profitability. A high level of cover - say 10 or 20 - gives much greater comfort, even when interest rates are relatively stable. The relationship between equity and dependence on external borrowing can be extended to include all external sources of funds by the Equity: Total assets ratio.

EQUITY/ TOTAL ASSETS

Equity / Total assets x 100

or

Owners' funds / Total assets x 100

This ratio is the converse of the Debt: Equity ratio. It identifies the percentage of the business' assets actually funded by the owners as opposed to lenders (including creditors).

The ultimate control over gearing in business is profit. A business that generates high profits will not need much in the way of borrowings. Where it does need to borrow, it will find it easy to do so. In contrast, a business that struggles to generate adequate profits will always have cash-flow difficulties. But, with its poor profit record, such a business will find it difficult to raise funds.

APPENDIX 2: USEFUL ADDRESSES

FINANCE
ACT VENTURE CAPITAL LTD - www.actventure.com
AIB BANK ENTERPRISE DEVELOPMENT BUREAU - www.aib.ie/roi/business/businessbanking.asp
ALLIANCE INVESTMENT CAPITAL - www.allinv.com
ANGLO IRISH BANK CORPORATION PLC - www.angloirishbank.ie
APAX PARTNERS & CO VENTURES (IRELAND) LTD - www.apax.com
BANK OF IRELAND ENTERPRISE SUPPORT UNIT - www.bankofireland.ie
BANK OF IRELAND ENTREPRENEURS FUND - www.delta.ie
BANK OF IRELAND NORTHERN IRELAND - www.bankofireland.co.uk
BANK OF SCOTLAND (IRELAND) LTD - www.bankofscotland.ie
BINARY PARTNERS - www.binary.ie
BUSINESS EXPANSION SCHEME - www.revenue.ie
BUSINESS INNOVATION FUND - www.dbic.ie
CAMPUS COMPANIES VENTURE CAPITAL FUND - www.campuscapital.com
CORPORATE FINANCE IRELAND - www.cfi.ie
CRESCENT CAPITAL - www.crescentcapital.co.uk
CROSS ATLANTIC CAPITAL PARTNERS - www.xacp.com
DELTA PARTNERS - www.delta.ie
DUBLIN SEED CAPITAL FUND - www.dbic.ie
EIRCOM ENTERPRISE FUND LTD - www.eircom-enterprise-fund.ie
EMERGING BUSINESS TRUST - www.mtf.com/ebt/index.htm
ENTERPRISE EQUITY - www.eeirl.com
FIRST TRUST BANK - www.ftbni.co.uk
GE CAPITAL WOODCHESTER - www.gecapital.com
GUINNESS ULSTER BANK EQUITY FUND - www.ncb.ie
HIBERNIA CAPITAL PARTNERS LTD - www.hcp.ie
IRISH BICS SEED CAPITAL FUND - www.dbic.ie
LOMBARD & ULSTER BANKING LTD - www.lombard.ie
MANAGEMENT TRAINING AND FINANCE GROUP - www.mtf.com
NATIONAL IRISH BANK LTD - www.nib.ie
NCB VENTURES - www.ncb.ie
NORTHERN BANK LTD - www.nbonline.co.uk
Permanent TSB BANK - www.permanenttsb.ie
SMALL ENTERPRISE SEED FUND - www.pdc.ie
TRINITY VENTURE CAPITAL LTD - www.tvc.com
ULSTER BANK - www.ulsterbank.com

INFORMATION
BELFAST BUSINESS LIBRARY
BELFAST FIRST STOP BUSINESS SHOP - www.firststopshop.co.uk
BUSINESS INFORMATION CENTRE - www.iol.ie/dublinsitylibrary/
BUSINESSINFORMATIONPOINT.COM - www.businessinformationpoint.com
GOVERNMENT (IRISH) WEBSITE - www.irlgov.ie
GOVERNMENT DIRECT FOR BUSINESS (NI) - www.nics.gov.uk/ni-direct/
HEALTH & SAFETY AUTHORITY - www.has.ie
HEALTH & SAFETY EXECUTIVE FOR NORTHERN IRELAND - www.hseni.gov.uk
LEGAL-ISLAND.COM - wwwlegal-island.com
OAK TREE PRESS - www.oaktreepress.com

NETWORKING
CHAMBERS OF COMMERCE OF IRELAND - www.chambersireland.ie
IRISH SMALL AND MEDIUM ENTERPRISES ASSOCIATION - www.isme.ie
NETWORK IRELAND - www.networkireland.ie
SMALL FIRMS ASSOCIATION - www.sfa.ie

SUPPORT
CITY/COUNTY ENTERPRISE BOARDS
ENTERPRISE IRELAND - www.enterprise-ireland.com
ENTERPRISE NORTHERN IRELAND - www.enterpriseni.com
EQUITYNETWORK - www.intertradeireland.com
INSTITUTE OF BUSINESS ADVISERS - www.iba.org.uk/branch50/ - www.iba.org.uk/branch55/
INSTITUTE OF DIRECTORS IN IRELAND - www.iodireland.ie
INTERTRADEIRELAND - www.intertradeireland.com
INVEST NORTHERN IRELAND - www.investni.com
NATIONAL INSTITUTE FOR TRANSPORT AND LOGISTICS - www.nitl.ie
PLATO IRELAND - www.plato.ie
SHANNON DEVELOPMENT - www.shannon-dev.ie
ÚDARÁS NA GAELTACHTA - www.udaras.ie

www.oaktreepress.com

e returned on
e tamped

OAK TREE PRE

Ireland's leading business book publisher,
Oak Tree Press is increasingly an international developer and
publisher of enterprise training and support
solutions.

Oak Tree Press has developed "platforms" of
Pre-start-up, Start-up, Growth and Support content.

These platforms include:
Publications; Websites; Software;
Assessment models; Training;
Consultancy and Certification.

The platforms allow different levels of entry from the
simple to quite complex, to meet different user needs.

Oak Tree Press' enterprise training and support solutions are
in use in Ireland, the UK, USA, Scandinavia and Eastern
Europe and are available for customisation to
local situations and needs.

For further information, contact:
Ron Immink or Brian O'Kane.

OAK TREE PRESS
19 Rutland Street, Cork, Ireland
T: + 353 21 431 3855   F: + 353 21 431 3496
E: info@oaktreepress.com   W: www.oaktreepress.com